D0268979

Le grand mystère
de Rosalie

la courte échelle

Les éditions de la courte échelle inc.
160, rue Saint-Viateur Est, bureau 404
Montréal (Québec) H2T 1A8
www.courteechelle.com

Dépôt légal, 4ᵉ trimestre 2012
Bibliothèque nationale du Québec

Copyright © 2012 Les éditions de la courte échelle inc.

La courte échelle reconnaît l'aide financière du gouvernement du Canada
par l'entremise du Fonds du livre du Canada pour ses activités d'édition.
La courte échelle est aussi inscrite au programme de subvention globale
du Conseil des arts du Canada et reçoit l'appui du gouvernement
du Québec par l'intermédiaire de la SODEC.

La courte échelle bénéficie également du Programme de crédit d'impôt
pour l'édition de livres — Gestion SODEC — du gouvernement du Québec.

**Catalogage avant publication de Bibliothèque et Archives nationales
du Québec et Bibliothèque et Archives Canada**

Anfousse, Ginette
    Le grand mystère de Rosalie
    Pour les jeunes de 9 ans et plus.
    ISBN 978-2-89651-918-7
    I. Sarrazin, Marisol. II. Titre. Titre. III. Collection: Roman Jeunesse.

PS8551.N42G722 2012   jC843'.54   C2012-940707-0
PS9551.N42G722 2012

Imprimé au Canada

Ginette Anfousse

Lorsque Ginette Anfousse était enfant, elle suivait des cours de danse et rêvait de devenir ballerine. Mais la vie l'a menée vers deux autres passions : l'écriture et le dessin. Aujourd'hui, Ginette danse avec les mots ! Elle poursuit une carrière d'écrivaine dans sa maison des Laurentides, au bord d'un lac paisible. Ses idées peuvent surgir n'importe quand, mais c'est le matin qu'elle préfère s'isoler pour écrire. Dans l'atelier silencieux, la chienne Charlotte attend patiemment que sa maîtresse soit sortie de ses histoires pour aller faire de longues promenades et cueillir des framboises, leur fruit favori.

Marisol Sarrazin

Marisol Sarrazin a grandi dans les Laurentides, entourée de parents qui dessinaient et écrivaient. Touche-à-tout, elle a fait des détours par la sculpture, la mise en scène, le théâtre, le cinéma, la danse, avant de se consacrer à l'illustration. Aujourd'hui, elle travaille beaucoup avec différents auteurs, dont sa mère, Ginette Anfousse. De la fenêtre de son atelier entouré par la nature, Marisol voit passer des renards et parfois même des ours…, peut-être attirés par le chocolat dont elle raffole.

De la même auteure, à la courte échelle

Collection Tout carton
Série Polo Pépin :
Polo et l'anniversaire
Polo et le panier de fruits
Polo à la ferme
Polo et la musique
Polo et la fête de la citrouille
Polo et le bonhomme de neige

Collection Albums
Série Jiji et Pichou :
Mon ami Pichou
La cachette
La chicane
La varicelle
Le savon
L'hiver ou le bonhomme Sept Heures
L'école
La fête
La petite sœur
Je boude
Devine ?
La grande aventure
Le père Noël

Série Polo Pépin :
Polo et le Roulouboulou
Polo et le garde-manger
Polo et l'écureuil volant
Polo au zoo

Collection Premier Roman
Série Arthur :
Le père d'Arthur
Les barricades d'Arthur
Le chien d'Arthur

Collection Roman Jeunesse
Série Rosalie :
Les catastrophes de Rosalie
Le héros de Rosalie
Rosalie s'en va-t-en guerre
Les vacances de Rosalie
Le grand rêve de Rosalie
Rosalie à la belle étoile
Le grand roman d'amour de Rosalie
La grande frousse de Rosalie

Hors collection Roman Jeunesse
Série Rosalie :
Rosalie, volume 1
Rosalie, volume 2
Rosalie, volume 3

Collection Ado
Un terrible secret

Rosalie voyage autour du monde…

Les lecteurs de nombreux pays connaissent bien Rosalie, puisque ses aventures sont traduites en anglais, en espagnol, en italien, en allemand, en grec et en chinois.

Ginette Anfousse à l'honneur !

- Sélection IBBY Canada (section nationale de l'Union internationale pour les livres de jeunesse) « Livres d'images canadiens remarquables » pour *Polo et le Roulouboulou* (2003)

- Sceau d'argent, Prix du livre M. Christie pour *Polo et le Roulouboulou* (2003)

- Finaliste du Prix du livre M. Christie pour *Les barricades d'Arthur* (1993)

- Lauréate du prix La bibliothèque du parfait Montréalais pour *Les catastrophes de Rosalie* (1992)

- Finaliste du Prix du Gouverneur général du Canada — catégorie Littérature jeunesse (texte) pour *Un terrible secret* (1991)

- Prix du livre M. Christie pour *Rosalie s'en va-t-en guerre* (1990)

- Prix Québec/Wallonie-Bruxelles pour *Les catastrophes de Rosalie* (1988)

- Prix Fleury-Mesplet, meilleure auteure jeunesse des dix dernières années au Québec (1987)

- Liste d'honneur IBBY, pour *La chicane* (1978)

- Prix du Conseil des arts du Canada pour *La varicelle* et *La chicane* (1978)

Pour en savoir plus sur la série Rosalie,
visitez www.courteechelle.com/collection-roman-jeunesse

Ginette Anfousse

LE GRAND MYSTÈRE DE ROSALIE

Illustrations de Marisol Sarrazin

la courte échelle

Prologue

Il me restait à peine deux jours avant notre grand départ vers Cap-au-Renard pour persuader mes sept tantes de me laisser chez mon amie Julie. Après mille simagrées, cent supplications et une bonne dizaine de « je le jure », j'ai réussi.

Pendant qu'elles prendront l'avion vers le salon funéraire d'un petit village perdu de la Gaspésie, moi je camperai toute la fin de semaine chez ma meilleure amie.

Après tout, Rosaire-Timothée Dansereau, je ne l'ai jamais connu. Le pauvre avait 107 ans et des poussières quand il est mort dans son sommeil, ne laissant personne derrière lui.

C'est le père de Julie qui a semé le doute dans la tête de mes tantes. Je l'avais supplié de me suivre à la maison, de leur expliquer mon point de vue et surtout de les rassurer toutes les sept. Il a plaidé, super convaincant :

— Il sera toujours temps pour Rosalie de se familiariser avec la mort. Elle est si sensible.

Et parce qu'il les savait hyper mères poules, il a ajouté :

— Vous n'avez pas à vous inquiéter, Rosalie est comme notre fille. Et trois jours, c'est si vite passé. .

J'en ai profité pour ajouter que les vrais cercueils et les églises me donnaient la chair de poule. Qu'en plus j'avais une peur bleue des avions. Après avoir perdu mon vrai père et ma vraie mère dans le pire accident aérien que le Québec ait connu, c'était facile à comprendre.

J'ai évité de parler de la super-fête que les parents de Kan Shou avaient organisée pour son anniversaire, samedi. J'ai seulement dit que c'était normal chez les jeunes de mon âge de préférer le plaisir au chagrin. Que le père de Julie avait raison, j'avais le restant de ma vie pour m'accoutumer au malheur.

Finalement, après m'avoir fait jurer dix fois de me coucher avant onze heures, de ne pas déranger avec mes questions, de faire mon lit, de ramasser mes traîneries, de me brosser les dents et de toujours dire « s'il vous plaît » et « merci », mes sept tantes ont dit oui.

Le grand mystère de Rosalie

Chapitre I
Ma première nuit
chez Julie

Vendredi soir, dix minutes avant le départ de la nouvelle fourgonnette de mes tantes pour l'aéroport de Montréal, j'ai sonné chez Julie. D'une main, je tenais mon sac à dos, mes deux DVD de *Twilight* et mes patins à roues alignées. De l'autre, mon chat, sa litière, ses galettes de poisson, son poteau à griffes et sa souris Mickey.

Madame Morin a d'abord lorgné mon bagage, puis jeté un regard appuyé sur Charbon avant de m'aviser en reculant :

— Tu veux bien, Rosalie, installer ton chat dans le sous-sol. Pas que j'ai peur de ces petites bêtes, mais depuis un certain temps, je suis allergique au poil des animaux. Toi, tu pourras dormir en haut, dans la chambre de Julie.

Sur le coup je n'ai rien dit. Mais plus tard, on a décidé, Julie et moi, de passer la nuit dans le sous-sol avec mon chat.

Bien étendues sur le futon devant le cinéma maison, on a visionné, coup sur coup, « Fascination » et « Tentation », que mes tantes m'avaient loués exprès pour l'occasion. On les a regardés même si mon amie n'a pas cessé de râler sur l'invraisemblance des scénarios. Elle est comme ça, Julie, toujours à râler sur quelque chose. Même sur la beauté hallucinante de Robert Pattinson, qu'elle trouve, elle, super pâlot et super mièvre.

Je n'avais pas très envie de m'obstiner. J'ai fait remarquer que Théo Bergeron, le nouveau chum de Marie-Ève Poirier, avec sa petite coupe de cheveux et ses yeux en amande, lui ressemblait comme deux gouttes d'eau.

J'ai ajouté que depuis son retour des États-Unis, la chipie n'avait pas perdu de temps, que Théo était déjà son troisième amoureux.

Julie a haussé les épaules et marmonné qu'elle ne l'avait pas encore rencontré. Qu'au fond c'était le dernier de ses soucis. N'empêche, j'étais sûre et certaine que le lendemain, elle le verrait à la fête de Kan Shou. Sa mère avait quasiment invité la moitié de l'école Reine-Marie.

Je n'ai pas eu le temps de le dire à mon amie, mais j'en voulais beaucoup à Pierre-Yves Hamel d'avoir préféré passer son week-end dans les

Laurentides. Depuis son retour du pays des kangourous et des wallabies, mon supposé amoureux capote sur le canot, le kayak et la plongée sous-marine. Moi, j'haïs l'eau et je nage encore comme un marteau. Je me demande si le beau Théo Bergeron préfère comme moi le plancher des vaches.

* * *

Après quatre heures de cinéma, deux heures de placotage sur nos profs de gym et de géo, sur le *piercing* inattendu de Miss Lessing et surtout sur le nouveau tatouage de Marie-Ève Poirier, *I love la Californie*, il était quasiment une heure du matin.

On allait s'installer pour la nuit quand j'ai sorti la fameuse barrette en strass que j'avais choisie d'offrir à Kan Shou. Julie l'a trouvée super. Elle aurait bien voulu me montrer la photo qu'elle avait prise de Wouf, le basset de Kan Shou, mais elle avait décidé, à la dernière minute, de la faire laminer chez Lorenzo Photo. Le cadeau devait être prêt le lendemain matin, et j'ai promis d'aller le récupérer avec elle.

On allait se glisser sous les couvertures quand elle a demandé, comme si c'était d'une urgence capitale :

— C'était qui, Rosaire-Timothée Dansereau ?

J'ai répondu :

— Ben, le mort de Cap-au-Renard, c't'affaire !

Et j'ai ajouté en rigolant :

— Avec un prénom comme ça, sûrement le plus vieux mort de la Gaspésie !

Je savais bien que mon amie voulait savoir quel lien Rosaire-Timothée Dansereau avait avec ma famille.

J'ai raconté que je ne connaissais pas grand-chose à la généalogie des Dansereau et j'ai précisé, agacée, que le boulevard Saint-Joseph était pas mal loin de la Gaspésie. Que non seulement je n'avais pas connu mon grand-père et ma

Le grand mystère de Rosalie

grand-mère Dansereau, mais que je ne connaissais absolument personne de la famille de mon père. Sauf mes tantes, évidemment.

Julie, butée, a continué :

— Et la famille de ta mère, elle ? Me semble que tu n'en parles jamais…

J'ai hésité avant de lui avouer, honteuse, que j'en savais encore moins. Seulement que ma mère venait, comme mes tantes l'avaient raconté, d'un vieux pays et que mon père l'avait rencontrée là-bas.

Pour clore la discussion, j'ai attrapé Charbon et je me suis retournée vers le mur en soupirant :

— Si ça ne te fait rien, Julie Morin, j'aimerais changer de sujet.

Elle a glissé ses lunettes dans son étui, tiré les couvertures sur son menton avant de bougonner, vexée :

— J'ai une mémoire d'éléphant, Rosalie Dansereau, et si j'ai toujours supposé que ta mère venait, elle aussi, de la Gaspésie… c'est que tu ne m'avais jamais dit qu'elle venait d'un vieux pays.

D'un geste sec, ma meilleure amie a éteint la dernière lumière du sous-sol. Dix secondes plus tard, la sapristi de mocheté de reine des questionneuses rêvait aux anges. Moi, je n'arrivais pas à dormir, je pensais à toutes les questions sur ma mère que j'aurais dû poser à mes tantes.

Chapitre II
Chez Lorenzo Photo

À midi pile le lendemain, on s'est réveillées en catastrophe. Je ne saurai jamais ce qui s'est passé. Charbon miaulait, feulait, crachait pendant que la mère de Julie, coincée dans l'escalier, lançait des hurlements aussi perçants qu'une sirène de pompier. Heureusement, l'arrivée du père de Julie a calmé un peu les choses.

J'en ai profité pour attraper Charbon et le pousser subito presto par la fenêtre qui donne sur la ruelle. J'ai promis que mon chat n'entrerait plus jamais dans leur maison. De toute façon, Charbon préfère de loin rester à l'extérieur. Surtout au printemps. Ça lui arrive même de courir la galipote et de disparaître pendant des jours.

Le calme revenu, on s'est habillées en vitesse. On a avalé la pile de crêpes que madame Morin avait cuisinées pour nous. En rangeant la vaisselle, on a réalisé qu'il nous restait à peine une petite heure pour courir chez Lorenzo Photo et revenir se pomponner pour la fête de Kan Shou.

* * *

C'est moi, pour gagner du temps, qui ai proposé d'enfiler nos patins. Je me demande maintenant si c'était une bonne idée. Bref, on filait l'une derrière l'autre sur la rue Mont-Royal quand le drôle d'accident est arrivé.

Pour éviter de foncer dans une poussette, j'ai bousculé Julie. Elle s'est retrouvée... pataff ! sur le derrière. Ses lunettes ont fait un court vol plané avant d'atterrir, croyez-le ou non, aux pieds de Théo Bergeron.

Et là j'ai vu, de mes yeux vu, celui qui ressemble comme deux gouttes d'eau au célèbre vampire se pencher vers Julie, ramasser ses lunettes, les lui replacer sur le bout du nez en murmurant :

— Tu as les plus beaux yeux que j'aie jamais vus.

Il l'a ensuite aidée à se remettre sur ses patins et, ma foi, il était temps que Marie-Ève Poirier rapplique pour les séparer. Ma meilleure amie, les joues en feu, les yeux dans la graisse de bines, loin de le trouver mièvre venait de lui répondre :

— Toi aussi !

J'ai tiré Julie par la manche. En furie, Marie-Ève tirait, elle, son beau Théo dans la direction opposée. Trois minutes plus tard, ma meilleure amie avait très légèrement retrouvé ses esprits, et on entrait toutes les deux chez le marchand de photos.

Pendant que Julie attendait au comptoir pour récupérer le fameux cadeau de Kan Shou, je suis allée fouiner au fond du magasin. Plus précisément dans le coin le plus sombre, où j'avais remarqué un amoncellement de cadres biscornus mettant plus ou moins en valeur un tas de vieilles photos. Je farfouillais dans ce bric-à-brac quand une image a attiré mon attention.

En m'approchant, j'ai reconnu, déconcertée, la réplique de la photo que mes tantes avaient accrochée, depuis des lunes, sur le mur de ma chambre. Celle où entre ma mère et mon père, je mâchouille une suce en braillant.

Mes tantes avaient toujours affirmé que c'était l'unique photo qui existait de moi avec mes parents. Qu'on l'avait prise la veille de leur terrible accident.

Une dizaine de minutes plus tard, Julie m'a trouvée perdue dans mes pensées. Elle a dit, dépitée :

— Je t'ai cherchée partout ! Tu veux me dire ce que tu fais assise par terre ?

J'ai fait un geste vers le cadre.

— Ça te rappelle quelque chose ?

Mon amie a pris une seconde pour l'examiner :

— Ouais ! C'est presque une réplique de la photo accrochée sur le mur de ta chambre.

J'ai dit, perplexe :

— Comment ça, presque ?

Elle a précisé que sur cette photo le bébé ne pleurnichait pas, qu'il était même souriant.

J'ai à peine eu le temps de lui dire qu'il n'y avait jamais eu d'autres photos. Qu'on me l'avait répété mille fois. Mais sans égard pour mon désarroi, Julie m'a attrapée par la manche en disant qu'on était assez en retard comme ça. Qu'on avait toute la journée du lendemain pour revenir et chercher une explication.

En filant sur Mont-Royal, toujours en patins, mille sapristi de mochetés de mauvaises choses me trottaient dans la tête. Surtout, je n'arrivais pas à croire que mes tantes m'avaient raconté des histoires.

Chapitre III
Des tas de chichis

Difficile à imaginer, mais je n'ai jamais vu mon amie faire autant de chichis. Installée devant son miroir, elle trouvait son jean pas assez ceci, ses cheveux pas assez cela…

Pire, elle capotait sur son nez, ses hanches, son ventre. Sur toute sa personne, sauf sur ses yeux. Qui, tout à coup, étaient devenus super merveilleux.

D'habitude, les discussions sur les garçons lui passaient par-dessus la tête, et son unique histoire d'amour avait duré soixante-douze minutes. C'était avec Pedro Cortez, juste avant la soirée d'Halloween chez Marco Tifo l'automne dernier.

Maintenant, la reine de la logique et des mathématiques n'arrêtait pas de me bombarder de questions. Elle voulait savoir si les coups de foudre existaient vraiment. Si à presque douze ans on pouvait réellement tomber amoureux.

Si elle était assez belle. Assez mince. Assez fine. Assez tout pour intéresser un garçon.

Et j'ai failli m'étouffer quand elle a demandé :

— Crois-tu, Rosalie Dansereau, qu'un garçon comme Théo Bergeron peut vraiment aimer une fille comme moi ?

J'ai compris que c'était bel et bien fini, la Julie toujours au-dessus de ses affaires. La Julie super arrogante, super moqueuse, super rassurante et toujours prête à s'oublier pour me sauver la vie.

Chaque fois que je tentais de lui parler de la fameuse photo, elle me rabrouait en faisant bifurquer la conversation sur qui vous savez.

Bref, pendant que je vivais peut-être la pire crise de mon existence, elle, devant son miroir, bougonnait en triturant une mèche de ses cheveux, son jean ou son chandail.

Elle n'arrêtait pas de demander :

— Tu es certaine qu'il sera au *party* ? J'ai la trouille, Rosalie ! J'ai le cœur, je te jure, qui joue au yoyo.

D'habitude, c'est moi l'hyper émotive. Moi qui doute de tout, qui m'illusionne, qui fabule, qui exagère, qui en mets trop.

Encore pire, elle qui ne se maquille jamais a osé me demander de dessiner un trait de khôl

Le grand mystère de Rosalie

et d'ajouter un peu d'ombre sur ses paupières. Heureusement, la mère de Julie, dans sa trousse de beauté, avait tout ce qu'il fallait. J'ai même appliqué, en plus, un *gloss* rosé sur ses lèvres et du fard de la même couleur sur ses joues.

Elle s'est examinée longtemps, collée sur son miroir, avant de m'annoncer en papillonnant des yeux :

— Myope ou pas, c'est décidé, je vais au *party* sans mes lunettes !

Et rien à faire, rien à dire pour la décourager. Ne pas distinguer à dix centimètres une pomme d'une orange était devenu le dernier de ses soucis.

On était presque rendues chez Kan Shou quand Julie s'est aperçue qu'elle avait oublié son cadeau. On est revenues sur nos pas reprendre la fameuse photo de Wouf. Le *party* était commencé depuis belle lurette quand on est arrivées.

Chapitre IV
Chez Kan Shou Li

Tout de suite en entrant chez Kan Shou, j'ai réalisé que ma meilleure amie avait eu une sapristi de mocheté de bonne idée de laisser ses lunettes quelque part dans sa chambre. Impossible pour elle de voir la vingtaine de filles pâmées qui tournaient autour de Théo Bergeron.

On a déposé nos cadeaux, et par mesure de sécurité j'ai poussé Julie à l'écart. Histoire de lui éviter le choc d'une future première vraie peine d'amour, je l'ai installée pile à côté du bol de chips BBQ, ses croustilles préférées.

J'ai brandi le bol sous son nez, mais ma meilleure amie a refusé carrément d'en avaler. Elle se plaignait aussi de l'odeur du maïs soufflé, des colas et du punch aux fruits, qui lui donnait étrangement la nausée. De plus, elle n'arrêtait pas d'étirer le cou, de trépigner. Je savais bien qu'elle cherchait son Théo parmi la quarantaine d'invités qui se dandinaient sur la musique.

Il y avait tellement de monde tassé comme des sardines dans le sous-sol des Li que c'est à peine si, l'espace d'une seconde, on a pu entrevoir Kan Shou. De temps à autre, j'apercevais Marco Tifo, Marise Cormier, Olivier Primeau-Cadieux ou Pedro Cortez, qui me faisaient des signes. Ils dansaient et rigolaient comme des fous.

De loin, comme ça, le beau Théo n'avait pas l'air de s'amuser lui non plus. Marie-Ève Poirier le surveillait de près. Même qu'elle se démenait comme un diable dans l'eau bénite pour empêcher les autres filles de l'approcher.

Quand la musique s'est arrêtée, Julie en a profité pour me chuchoter à l'oreille :

— … le vois-tu ?

J'ai fait mine de ne pas comprendre. Puis j'ai haussé les épaules en secouant la tête.

Elle a marmonné :

— Arrête de finasser, Rosalie Dansereau, je sais qu'il est ici. J'en ai même la certitude.

J'allais me résoudre à la conduire vers son Roméo quand j'ai aperçu Marie-Ève Poirier, les baguettes en l'air, qui fonçait droit sur nous.

J'ai prévenu Julie :

— Prépare-toi, Marie-Ève approche ! Si tu avais mis tes lunettes, tu pourrais apprécier son regard assassin.

Je n'ai pas eu le temps de développer que la chipie apostrophait mon amie en hurlant :

— Tu te prends pour qui ? T'es peut-être la bolée de l'école Reine-Marie, mais t'as besoin de te lever de bonne heure pour voler ce qui m'appartient.

Ç'a été plus fort que moi, j'ai lancé en ricanant :

— On aimerait bien savoir de qui tu parles, Marie-Ève Poirier !

Elle a répliqué, déchaînée :

— Toi, tais-toi ! Julie Morin sait très bien de qui je parle.

Puis, m'écartant, elle s'est mise à lui crier par la tête :

— C'était *looser* à mort de faire semblant de te casser la margoulette en patins pour attirer son attention. De toute façon, avec un *look* de *nerd* comme le tien, ce n'est pas toi qui feras tripper Théo Bergeron.

Et juste avant de tourner les talons :

— Même maquillée, même sans lunettes, tu es aussi *cool* qu'une patate !

Le grand mystère de Rosalie

Sur le coup j'ai figé net, Julie aussi. Mais la chipie n'est pas allée très loin. Je l'ai attrapée par le collet et j'allais lui crêper le chignon quand toutes les lumières du sous-sol se sont éteintes.

La mère de Kan Shou, un énorme gâteau scintillant dans les mains, est apparue en chantant : « Ma chère Kan Shou, c'est à ton tour de te laisser parler d'amour ».

Marie-Ève Poirier a eu la chance de sa vie, j'allais l'étriper. Enfin, j'ai lâché sa tignasse et j'ai chanté avec tout le monde.

Après, Kan Shou a soufflé ses 12 chandelles. On a rallumé les lumières et elle a commencé à déballer ses cadeaux. Il y en avait 43 en tout. Par un hasard de tous les diables, les deux derniers étaient celui de Julie et celui de Théo.

Et par un autre hasard de tous les diables, Julie et Théo avaient eu la même idée : prendre une photo de Wouf, le chien de Kan Shou, et la faire laminer.

J'avoue qu'après il y a eu un moment de grande magie. Théo s'est approché de mon amie et lui a soufflé quelques mots à l'oreille. Je ne sais pas ce qu'il a dit, mais les yeux de Julie se sont allumés comme deux étoiles dans la nuit.

Ils pétillaient encore quand Marie-Ève Poirier, malade de jalousie, s'est avancée en cati-mini pour l'aviser :

— Tu te penses *too much*, mais j'ai 285 amis sur Facebook. Je te promets que les 285 vont entendre parler de toi et de tes manigances.

Ma meilleure amie était beaucoup trop partie dans les nuages pour s'inquiéter. Je dirais même qu'elle flottait à des dizaines d'années-lumière, au fin fond de la galaxie.

Finalement, le *party* s'est terminé vers 17 heures et c'est à peine si j'ai pu reparler à Julie, tant elle et Théo avaient de choses à se raconter.

En sortant, ils ont même décidé de faire un petit détour par le parc Laurier. Je n'avais pas l'intention de jouer les casse-pieds. Je n'avais pas non plus envie de rentrer toute seule chez ses parents. J'ai bifurqué vers la rue Mont-Royal en espérant arriver avant la fermeture de Lorenzo Photo.

À la porte du magasin, j'ai frappé de toutes mes forces. Quelqu'un à l'intérieur m'a fait signe que c'était fermé. Écœurée, j'ai ravalé ma salive.

Malgré les rayons du soleil de mai qui enflammaient la façade des maisons, malgré l'odeur sucrée des lilas en fleurs, malgré les groupes d'enfants qui riaient en se poursuivant dans la rue, je me suis sentie abandonnée. Abandonnée par Pierre-Yves Hamel. Abandonnée par mes tantes. Abandonnée par ma meilleure amie.

Chapitre V
Le beau Théo

Arrivée chez les Morin, j'ai sonné. Surprise : c'est Julie en personne qui s'est pointée. Elle avait remis ses lunettes.

J'ai dit :

— Déjà revenue !

Elle a répondu :

— Ouais… Pas parce que je suis amoureuse que je vais laisser tomber ma meilleure amie.

J'ai presque eu envie de lui sauter au cou. J'ai seulement dit :

— Me suis rendue au magasin de photo. Poche ! C'était fermé. J'y retournerai demain.

Et, comme chez les Morin on mange tôt, on est passées à table illico. Julie, la tête ailleurs, a tripoté longtemps dans son assiette, avant de la repousser en soupirant :

— Désolée m'man, j'ai l'estomac à l'envers. Trop bouffé de cochonneries chez les Li.

Je savais qu'à la fête, Julie n'avait rien avalé. Facile à comprendre, elle est en amour. Comme je n'avais pas très faim moi non plus, j'ai renchéri, racontant qu'on avait mangé à deux une bonne dizaine de rouleaux de printemps, une vingtaine de crevettes à la citronnelle, une quarantaine de pousses de bambou et six ou sept portions de gâteau à la mandarine.

Après, je ne savais plus quoi dire, Julie non plus. On avait tellement hâte toutes les deux de se retrouver sans parents ni rien. On avait tellement de choses à se raconter. C'est peut-être pour ça que monsieur Morin a passé son temps à nous taquiner. Il nous trouvait pas mal mystérieuses et un peu trop silencieuses à son goût.

Le repas terminé, je n'ai jamais vu un lave-vaisselle se faire remplir si rapidement. Ni une Julie Morin débouler un escalier et courir aussi vite à son ordi. Elle avait donné son adresse électronique à Théo et, la pauvre, elle espérait déjà recevoir un petit mot.

C'est plutôt un courriel pas rigolo qui l'attendait. Un courriel que l'expéditeur n'avait pas signé et qui la traitait de courailleuse ! De voleuse de chums ! On avait même ajouté que malgré ses airs de sainte nitouche, tout le boule-vard Saint-Joseph saurait bientôt quelle véritable hypocrite elle était.

Ce n'était pas difficile de deviner le nom de la frustrée, de l'hyper jalouse qui n'avait pas eu le courage de signer.

En un clic, Julie a fait disparaître le courriel. Puis dans un coin du sous-sol, pendant quasiment une heure, je l'ai laissé raconter les quinze fameuses minutes qu'elle avait passées au parc Laurier en tête à tête avec son Théo.

J'ai appris qu'il venait de la ville de Québec. Qu'il était, comme mon amie, enfant unique et un super-crac en informatique. Qu'il jouait de la clarinette. Qu'il aimait le football et les échecs.

J'ai aussi appris qu'il n'était ni pédant ni pré-tentieux et qu'il était beaucoup moins sûr de lui qu'on pouvait le supposer. Julie le croyait même un peu timide.

Elle charriait un brin, mon amie Julie. Pen-dant la fête chez les Li, j'avais eu tout mon temps pour l'épier. Avec toutes ces filles qui lui tournaient autour, difficile d'imaginer Théo Bergeron gêné.

Pour vérifier le degré de sa mauvaise foi, j'ai demandé, mine de rien :

— Maintenant que tu le connais mieux, sa ressemblance avec le beau Robert Pattinson doit te sauter aux yeux ?

Elle a secoué la tête à trois reprises avant d'éclater de rire.

— T'es folle, Rosalie Dansereau ! Théo est un million de fois plus beau !

Après, ma meilleure amie était plutôt contente de m'annoncer qu'il n'avait jamais eu d'histoire d'amour, ni de flirt, ni rien avec Marie-Ève Poirier. Que depuis son arrivée dans le quartier, elle disait seulement vouloir l'aider à s'intégrer à son groupe d'amis. Du moins, c'est ce que Théo en avait compris. Nous, on était certaines que Marie-Ève avait tenté par tous les moyens de lui mettre le grappin dessus.

Enfin, ça me chicotait drôlement de savoir ce que Théo lui avait chuchoté à l'oreille à la fête de Kan Shou, mais elle a dit, contrariée :

— … trop personnel, Rosalie Dansereau !

J'ai répliqué :

— Même pour ta meilleure amie ?

Elle a répété :

— Même pour ma meilleure amie.

J'ai grimacé, déçue. Puis j'ai pensé qu'elle avait sérieusement perdu la tête. J'en ai eu la certitude quand, quelques minutes plus tard, elle a attrapé les deux films de vampires qu'on avait vus la veille en disant :

— Si on les regardait de nouveau ?

On a visionné le premier DVD attentivement. Le deuxième venait à peine de commencer quand le père de Julie nous a retrouvées endormies collées l'une contre l'autre comme des bébés. C'est lui qui a éteint la télé.

Chapitre VI
Une mauvaise nuit

Julie la première s'est réveillée au milieu de la nuit. Elle a dit en me secouant :

— Réveille, Rosalie ! Réveille ! J'ai quelque chose d'hyper important à te demander.

J'ai bougonné :

— Ça pourrait pas attendre à demain matin ?

Elle a répondu :

— Non ! Ça urge ! C'est rapport à ta tante Florence. Celle qui fait tourner les tables et qui lit dans les lignes de la main. J'ai toujours pensé que ses supposés pouvoirs étaient une supercherie. Mais maintenant, je me dis qu'on ne sait jamais.

Elle a étiré le bras vers l'interrupteur et allumé toutes les lumières du sous-sol en demandant :

— Penses-tu qu'elle accepterait, avec des cartes ou sa boule de cristal, de me révéler deux ou trois choses concernant mon avenir ? Je parle de mon histoire avec Théo, bien entendu.

J'ai marmonné, dépitée :

— T'es sérieuse ?

Et là, croyez-le ou non, elle a soupiré :

— Bien, il arrive parfois que certains événements de la vie nous font changer d'idée.

— Même au milieu de la nuit ?

— Surtout au milieu de la nuit.

Pour en finir, j'ai promis qu'aussitôt tante Flo revenue de Cap-au-Renard, elle l'aurait, sa séance de cartomancie.

J'ai ramené les couvertures par-dessus ma tête et je me suis rendormie. Enfin je suppose, parce qu'un peu plus tard je me suis réveillée.

Le cœur me débattait. J'avais chaud. J'avais froid. Je tremblais. J'ai secoué Julie en hurlant d'allumer toutes les lumières. Que je capotais.

J'ai raconté que quelqu'un dans mon rêve avait ficelé un bébé comme une momie, qu'il l'avait déposé dans un panier. Qu'après, il avait poussé le panier sur l'eau en disant :

— Désolé ! Personne dans cette famille ne veut s'encombrer d'un bébé qui chiale.

Julie a dit :

— Je ne vois pas ce qu'il y a de paniquant là-dedans !

J'ai répondu en reniflant :

— Ce qu'il y a de paniquant, c'est que le panier s'est échoué pile sur le boulevard Saint-Joseph. Pile devant notre maison. Après, la porte s'est ouverte toute seule. Je n'ai pas été surprise d'apercevoir mes sept tantes cordées derrière. Seulement désemparée quand tante Béatrice s'est penchée vers le panier pour prendre le bébé, le soulever au-dessus de sa tête en disant : « Exactement celui qu'on avait commandé ! »

Toujours dans mon rêve, je me suis mise à crier, à hurler quand elle a ajouté : « C'est comme on avait dit, on l'appellera Rosalie. »

Julie a marmonné :

— Tu parles d'un drôle de rêve !

J'ai dit que ce n'était pas seulement un drôle de rêve. Ni un cauchemar. C'était une révélation. Une sapristi de mocheté de révélation.

Et j'ai ajouté, en larmes :

— La révélation, c'est que je ne suis pas une vraie Dansereau. Que mon vrai père et ma vraie mère n'ont jamais voulu de moi. Qu'ils m'ont abandonnée. Qu'ils sont quelque part en train d'aimer un autre enfant. Au fond, plus j'y pense, plus je réalise que mes tantes m'ont raconté des bobards. Des bobards sur la photo. Des bobards sur leur frère. Des bobards sur ma mère. Des bobards sur leur accident.

Julie m'a jeté un regard exaspéré.

— Tu ne trouves pas, Rosalie Dansereau, que tu exagères ? Me semble que tu n'as pas assez d'informations pour arriver à cette conclusion. C'était seulement un mauvais rêve. Pas une sapristi de mocheté de révélation, comme tu dis.

Elle a regretté immédiatement ses paroles. Piteuse, elle s'est approchée. Je l'ai repoussée. Si je n'avais pas mis Charbon à la rue, juré, j'aurais fini le reste de la nuit dans un coin du sous-sol, serrée contre lui.

Chapitre VII
Dimanche matin

Le lendemain matin, je filais un mauvais coton. J'avais mal à la tête. Julie avait raison, j'avais l'air d'un chien battu.

Elle, toujours aux petits oiseaux, venait de recevoir un premier courriel de son Théo. Elle m'a annoncé qu'il aimerait bien la revoir quelque part dans la journée. C'est tout ce qu'elle a voulu me dire. Le reste était encore une fois, je suppose, trop personnel.

Dépitée et peut-être un peu jalouse, je l'ai prévenue que j'étais capable de retourner toute seule chez le marchand de photos. Qu'à bien y penser, je n'avais pas besoin d'une Julie Morin pour mener mon enquête. Que, de toute façon, elle avait mieux à faire avec son Théo que d'entendre les divagations de sa meilleure amie.

Elle a dit en me fixant droit dans les yeux :
— T'es fâchée ?

J'ai répondu :

— Non !

Elle a répété, toquée :

— Oui, t'es fâchée ! Je le sais. La preuve, tes joues sont rouge tomate foncé, et tu voudrais prendre tes cliques et tes claques et retourner illico chez tes tantes. Sauf que... je n'ai pas l'intention de passer la journée en tête à tête avec mon Théo, comme tu dis. J'aime bien les enquêtes et j'ai décidé de t'aider.

Julie Morin avait raison, j'étais fâchée. Elle a toujours raison, d'ailleurs. Pour ne pas perdre totalement la face, j'ai fait diversion. J'ai déclaré que j'avais une faim de loup. Qu'on devrait monter à la cuisine et se préparer chacune un super-hot-dog moutarde-relish-ketchup-mayonnaise. Que c'était de ça que j'avais envie.

C'était pas mal idiot pour un petit déjeuner, surtout qu'elle n'avait pas d'appétit. Moi non plus. On a donc fourré les deux super-hot-dogs dans un sac plastique et, de nouveau complices, on a mis le tout, en rigolant, dans le frigo.

Puis on s'est habillées en vitesse. On a filé ensemble, et sans patins cette fois, chez Lorenzo Photo.

Il n'y avait presque personne dans le magasin. On a retrouvé assez facilement la fameuse photo. On a examiné le cadre sous tous ses angles. Il n'y avait rien de spécial. Que le prix exorbitant de 39,99 $.

Je me suis dirigée vers la caisse. J'ai dit au vieux monsieur qui se tenait derrière le comptoir :

— C'est pas un peu cher pour une si vieille photo ?

Il a répondu que c'était le cadre plaqué simili-or qui valait cher, pas l'image. Puis il a précisé, amusé, que la photo, elle, n'était pas si vieille que ça.

J'ai voulu savoir qui l'avait prise. Le pauvre l'ignorait. Julie, qui trépignait dans mon dos, a fini par demander :

— Est-ce possible, monsieur, d'acheter uniquement la photo ?

— Mais elle n'est pas à vendre, mademoiselle. C'est uniquement pour mettre le cadre en valeur.

Julie ne s'est pas laissé démonter. Avec un aplomb hallucinant, elle a prétendu qu'il y avait une grande histoire d'amour, une grande tragédie et un grand mystère concernant cette photo.

Le regard du vieux monsieur s'est allumé et il a demandé, malicieux :

— Un mystère comme un immense secret de famille, mademoiselle ?

C'est moi, le cœur battant, qui ai répondu :

— Oui, monsieur ! Exactement comme vous l'avez dit. Et l'immense secret de famille…, c'est moi.

Julie, de la tête, a fait signe que oui. Et j'ai raconté avec l'énergie du désespoir que j'avais le double de cette photo dans ma chambre. Que ma démarche n'était pas un caprice. Que depuis ma naissance, on m'avait raconté des bobards. Que cette deuxième photo en était la preuve. Bref, que pour moi c'était une question de vie ou de mort !

Julie Morin a encore une fois hoché la tête avant d'ajouter, les mains jointes et presque suppliante :

— Pourriez pas, monsieur, nous vendre le cadre… disons… 5,25 $? C'est tout l'argent qu'on a, à deux.

Ni l'une ni l'autre n'avions un sou dans les poches, mais Julie avait l'air de savoir exactement ce qu'elle faisait. N'empêche que j'ai failli m'étouffer quand elle a déclaré le plus sérieusement du monde :

— Vous savez, monsieur Lorenzo, ce qu'on soupçonne ? On soupçonne que la vraie mère de mon amie serait native, comme vous, de Turin, en Italie.

Pendant une éternité, les yeux dans le vide, le vieux monsieur s'est caressé la barbe. Puis il a attrapé le cadre, l'a mis dans un sac et l'a tendu vers moi en soupirant :

— Ma petite demoiselle, il n'y a pas de drame à être adoptée si vous n'êtes pas maltrai-tée. Et sachez qu'une maman italienne n'aban-donne jamais ses petits sans y être obligée.

Avant de se retirer au fond du magasin, il m'a souhaité bonne chance dans mes recherches. Nous, on lui a dit trois fois merci. Je me trompe peut-être, mais j'ai senti dans sa voix une immense tristesse.

Quand on est sorties dans la rue, j'avais un peu honte, mais la photo serrée sur le cœur, je jubilais.

C'est presque en arrivant chez Julie que je me suis demandé comment elle avait deviné pour monsieur Lorenzo, sa ville de Turin et son Italie.

Elle a dit :

— J'ai regardé, c't'affaire ! C'était écrit en toutes lettres sur la devanture du magasin :

Lorenzo Photo inc. Et juste en dessous: *De Turin à Montréal pour vous servir.*

J'ai insisté:

— OK pour Turin. Mais comment t'as fait pour l'Italie?

Elle s'est pris la tête à deux mains.

— Je me demande, Rosalie Dansereau, comment tu as fait pour gagner le dernier grand tournoi de géographie de l'école Reine-Marie!

Chapitre VIII
La fille de qui ?

On s'est installées dans la chambre de Julie avec une paire de pinces, des ciseaux et un couteau de cuisine. On ne savait pas au juste ce qui nous attendait, mais on était aussi fébriles qu'en déballant nos cadeaux de Noël.

J'ai d'abord constaté que Julie avait eu raison. La photo était presque la même que celle au-dessus de mon lit. Les parents avaient l'air un peu triste et le bébé, derrière sa suce, esquissait une sorte de sourire.

À quatre mains, on a démantelé le cadre, retiré le carton et dégagé délicatement la photo.

Nos cœurs ont bondi quand on a aperçu une drôle de signature au verso. Il nous a fallu

la super-loupe de monsieur Morin pour la déchiffrer. Finalement, on a réussi à lire : *Henri Lacasse, photographe*. Il y avait aussi une date, mais elle était quasi invisible.

J'ai dit, sans trop réfléchir :

— C'est bien beau un nom… mais ça nous mène à quoi ? On ne sait toujours pas si c'est vraiment moi qui souris sur cette photo. Ni si mes tantes ont tout manigancé. Ni si elles m'ont volée ou adoptée.

Julie m'a stoppée net.

— Tu ne vas pas recommencer avec tes histoires de révélation !

J'ai fait signe que non, mais j'ai ajouté, troublée :

— Veux-tu me dire, Julie Morin, pourquoi tante Alice, tante Béatrice, tante Colette, tante Diane, tante Élise, tante Florence et tante Gudule ne m'ont quasiment jamais parlé de ma vraie mère ? Pourquoi elles m'ont seulement répété qu'elle s'appelait Anne et qu'elles ne l'avaient pas très bien connue ?

Veux-tu m'expliquer pourquoi toutes les sept ne m'ont raconté que des banalités sur mon père ? Des insignifiances comme : « Si tu savais, ma soie, comme il était gentil ! Un vrai gentleman, mon ange ! Tu as sa tignasse noire, poison ! Et ses yeux malicieux, ma mouche ! Il t'aimait beaucoup, mon poussin ! Il était si fier de toi, mon oiseau des îles ! Ton père, mon cœur, c'était un cœur ! »

J'ai terminé, au bord des larmes :

— Et... ce n'est pas parce que mes tantes manquent de mémoire ou de vocabulaire, Julie Morin !

Malgré mon désarroi, Julie a tenté de me faire admettre que c'était peut-être un peu ma faute. Avant l'adolescence, on est moins curieux de ses origines. On serait comme des petits moineaux qui vivent au jour le jour. C'est du moins ce que son père lui avait déjà raconté.

J'ai annoncé, cramoisie, que mes tantes ne perdaient rien pour attendre. Que j'allais le soir même les mitrailler de questions. À moins que j'apprenne, d'ici leur retour, des choses tellement moches et pas géniales sur ma naissance que je prenne la poudre d'escampette pour toujours.

Julie a haussé les épaules.

— Arrête de dire des énormités, Rosalie Dansereau. On ne quitte pas les personnes qui nous aiment pour une photo inexpliquée. Si tu avais mieux dormi, tu dirais moins de niaiseries.

Pour la trentième fois de la journée, j'ai ravalé ma salive. Julie, les yeux mi-clos, s'est excusée. Je n'avais pas le choix, j'ai répondu OK.

C'est elle ensuite qui a proposé de chercher le numéro de téléphone de notre photographe sur son ordi. Elle répétait que joindre le bon Henri Lacasse nous aiderait drôlement à connaître la vérité sur le mystérieux trio de la photo.

Sur le site Canada 411, il y avait 46 Henri Lacasse, Julie les a comptés. Il était onze heures et quart quand on a commencé à téléphoner à tous ceux qui habitaient l'île de Montréal.

À midi, on n'avait pas encore trouvé le Henri Lacasse qu'on cherchait. On a décidé de remonter à la cuisine pour luncher. Sous l'œil décontenancé de madame Morin, on a glissé nos deux super-hot-dogs au micro-ondes. On est redescendues au sous-sol pour les manger. Comme Julie n'avait pas retrouvé l'appétit, j'ai avalé les deux.

Après, on a continué les appels qu'il nous restait dans le 514. Pour rien, d'ailleurs. Encore une fois, aucun des Henri Lacasse n'était photographe.

J'allais demander à mon amie : « On fait quoi, maintenant ? » Mais on sonnait à la porte, et à la vitesse où Julie Morin a disparu, j'ai compris que c'était son beau Théo qui rappliquait.

J'ai attendu une minute, puis deux, puis trois. Après, je me suis installée devant son ordi et pour passer le temps, j'ai tapé sur Google les lettres « DPJ ».

J'ai lu au premier article : *Enfants en difficulté*, puis au deuxième : *Comment faire un signalement*.

En songeant à toutes ces années passées avec mes tantes, je me suis creusé la cervelle pour imaginer un signalement un peu crédible. Mais malgré l'énormité de leurs mensonges, leurs punitions débiles et leur éducation super dépassée, je ne savais pas de quoi les accuser. Je veux dire sérieusement, comme si elles m'avaient battue.

Finalement, j'ai eu une meilleure idée, presque un éclair de génie. J'ai tapé, toujours sur Google : *Parents biologiques recherchés*. J'ai cliqué.

Ce qui est apparu m'a stupéfiée. Il y avait des dizaines et des dizaines de sites qui traitaient du sujet. Sur l'un d'eux, il y avait même 654 inscriptions de pères, de mères, de filles et de fils qui se cherchaient désespérément. On y donnait aussi des pistes pour aider dans ce qu'on qualifiait de démarche super délicate. Mais pour une raison que j'ignore, on devait avoir 18 ans pour s'inscrire et avoir accès aux informations.

Après dix minutes de lecture, de tâtonnement et de sapristi de mocheté de cafouillage, j'ai enfin déniché le site qui me convenait.

C'était une sorte de forum généalogique dans lequel on pouvait lire les témoignages de personnes qui cherchaient leurs parents. Ceux aussi de personnes qui les avaient trouvés.

N'importe qui pouvait s'inscrire et l'âge n'avait aucune importance. Mieux, non seulement je pouvais écrire MON histoire, mais elle pouvait être lue partout sur la planète.

Comme Julie n'arrivait toujours pas, j'ai décidé de composer un appel au secours. Au début, je ne savais pas par quel bout commencer, puis j'ai pris mon courage à deux mains et j'ai tapé :

Bonjour,

J'ai douze ans et j'ai soi-disant été adoptée par mes sept tantes. J'étais, paraît-il, l'enfant de leur frère aujourd'hui décédé et d'une mère, elle aussi décédée, qui venait d'ailleurs. Je pense d'un vieux pays.

Je ne crois pas mes tantes et je soupçonne que toutes ces histoires sont des racontars. Je pense qu'elles m'auraient peut-être achetée, volée, ou pire, kidnappée à mes vrais parents.

Pour l'instant je m'appelle Rosalie Dansereau, mais, au fond de mon cœur, je sens que ce n'est pas mon vrai nom. C'est pour retrouver mes parents biologiques, les voir et les aimer que j'envoie cet appel à l'aide.

P.-S. Si quelqu'un a besoin de mon ADN, je n'y vois pas d'inconvénient.

J'allais écrire toutes mes coordonnées quand Julie a fait irruption dans mon dos. Sans prendre le temps de poser une seule question, elle s'est mise à hurler :

— T'es nulle ou quoi ? Chercher tes vrais parents quand tu n'es sûre de rien ! Pire, quand tu as déjà sept mères qui t'adorent tellement que tu as du mal à les supporter !

Ensuite, elle s'est calmée un peu. Elle avait une bonne nouvelle à m'annoncer. Son Théo, qui s'intéressait à l'enquête, venait, paraît-il, de découvrir une piste de recherche super géniale et prometteuse. En attendant, je devais prendre mon mal en patience et surtout avoir une confiance absolue dans son nouvel amoureux.

Je ne voulais pas l'insulter, mais elle charriait de plus en plus, ma meilleure amie. J'ai quand même décidé de remettre à plus tard l'envoi de mon SOS à toute la planète. Julie a déclaré que c'était plus raisonnable. Après, elle a levé les yeux au ciel comme si je l'avais encore une fois super, hyper découragée.

Chapitre IX
Henri Lacasse
en Gaspésie?

Pendant que, scotché à son ordi, Théo Bergeron enquêtait de chez lui, nous, on a quand même continué de chercher notre Henri Lacasse en Gaspésie. Au fond, toute la famille Dansereau en était originaire.

Sur Canada 411, ce n'était pas chinois, il y avait un Henri Lacasse qui habitait à Matane, un autre à Gaspé et un troisième à Maria.

J'ai d'abord téléphoné à Maria. Une dame a répondu qu'il y avait pas un, mais deux Henri Lacasse dans la maison. Que le premier était peintre en bâtiment. Que le deuxième, pour l'instant, n'était pas photographe. Qu'il était plutôt préoccupé par son hochet et son biberon.

À Gaspé, je suis tombée sur un répondeur qui débitait : « Vous avez bien joint Henri Lacasse, ostéopathe, et sa famille. Pour un rendez-vous avec Henri, faites le 1. Pour annuler un rendez-vous, faites le 2. Pour laisser un message, faites le 3. Pour joindre Germaine, faites le 4. Pour Philippe, faites le 5. Pour Sophie, faites le 6. Pour… »

Excédée, j'ai raccroché et c'est Julie qui a pitonné, sans beaucoup d'espoir, le dernier numéro qu'on avait trouvé.

Elle est tombée sur une espèce d'énergumène qui s'est mise à pleurnicher en racontant, sans qu'on le lui demande, que son Henri était parti à l'aventure avec une certaine Colette, ou Georgette, ou Ginette Dubois-Tremblay. Comme le territoire de la Gaspésie est aussi grand que quatre fois la Suisse, elle souhaitait bonne chance à qui voulait le retrouver.

Julie a demandé le plus gentiment du monde s'il avait laissé un numéro de téléphone.

La folle a marmonné que de toute façon, elle ne le donnerait pas à n'importe qui.

Elle a même ajouté, retrouvant bizarrement son aplomb :

— La discrétion, mademoiselle, ça vous dit quelque chose ?

Julie a grimacé en disant :

— Excusez-moi, madame, mais si votre Henri Lacasse est photographe, ce numéro de téléphone est super important pour mon amie…

C'est qu'on enterre à l'instant même, à Cap-au-Renard, son oncle préféré.

La dame au bout du fil a fini par répondre, assez sèchement merci :

— Non, mademoiselle, mon Henri Lacasse n'était pas photographe.

Puis l'énergumène, sans tambour ni trompette, a raccroché.

Il était presque deux heures quand on a décidé de cesser nos recherches. Julie s'est installée à son ordi pour prendre ses nouveaux messages.

Il y en avait quatre. Un de la bibliothèque Le Petit Bonheur pour l'informer que le livre commandé était arrivé.

Un deuxième de Kan Shou la remerciant pour la photo de Wouf. Elle l'avait installée sur le mur de sa chambre à côté de celle de Théo.

Le troisième, moins jojo et particulièrement ratoureux, était de Marie-Ève Poirier.

Elle racontait qu'elle venait tout juste d'apprendre des choses graves sur Théo Bergeron. Des choses qui expliquaient peut-être son départ en catastrophe de la ville de Québec. Elle jurait qu'il ne fallait pas se fier à son sourire, à ses belles phrases et à ses beaux yeux. Que dans son cas, le proverbe «On n'attire pas les mouches avec du vinaigre» était super juste. Qu'enfin, Julie n'avait qu'à lui faire signe si elle voulait en apprendre davantage.

Elle s'excusait aussi de l'avoir bousculée à la fête de Kan Shou. Que c'était avant de savoir qui était vraiment Théo Bergeron.

C'est en ouvrant son quatrième message qu'on a compris le petit jeu tordu que Marie-Ève avait imaginé. C'était écrit :

Salut Julie,

Tu ne me connais pas, j'habite la ville de Québec. Je suis, à ma connaissance, l'avant-dernière ex de Théo Bergeron. J'ai le cœur brisé. Je suis full *malheureuse. Je ne mange plus. Je pense même me laisser mourir. Je ne suis pas la seule qu'il a trompée. Pas la seule à lui avoir fait confiance. On est déjà trente-deux à se consoler. À s'aider. À tenter de recoller les morceaux. À ne pas capoter. Quelques-unes ont même suggéré de fonder un site virtuel du genre* Les ex-trompées du beau Théo Bergeron.

Sûr et certain qu'on lui en veut à mort, mais c'est par solidarité qu'on a décidé, à l'avenir, d'aviser par courriel chacune de ses futures

victimes. Surtout celles qui se croient plus fu-
tées, plus intelligentes que les autres.

Un conseil : laisse-le avant de devenir son
trente-troisième trophée. N'oublie pas que le
monde est petit et que tout se sait.

Une full *déçue qui te veut du bien.*

Julie a éclaté de rire. Moi, je trouvais ça
chien en sapristi. On savait bien, toutes les
deux, que le courriel ne pouvait être qu'une
manigance de Marie-Ève Poirier. C'était son
style tout craché. N'empêche que pendant un
quart de seconde, je me suis demandé si, dans
ces niaiseries, il n'y avait pas une parcelle
de vérité. Après tout, on ne connaissait rien
de Théo Bergeron. Mais... à regarder l'assu-
rance impériale de mon amie, je n'ai rien dit.

Au moment où elle allait faire disparaître
ces deux courriels, je lui ai proposé de mettre
Théo au courant. Comme une bombe, Julie a
explosé :

— Jamais, tu entends, je ne lui ferai lire des
bêtises pareilles. Si jamais, Rosalie Dansereau,
tu as le malheur de lui en glisser un mot, je
t'arrache la langue. Et sérieux..., tu ne seras
plus jamais mon amie. Enfin presque plus
mon amie.

Dans une série de clics rageurs, elle a supprimé tous ses messages de la journée. Après, soulagée, elle a haussé les épaules.

— Je ne me fais pas d'illusions. Je sais qu'il y aura d'autres courriels aussi stupides. D'autres mensonges aussi bêtes qu'elle répétera sur Facebook à ses supposés 285 amis.

Connaissant toutes les vacheries que Marie-Ève Poirier m'avait fait subir par le passé, j'étais d'accord avec elle. On savait que la chipie inventerait ses méchancetés aussi longtemps qu'elle n'aurait pas mis le grappin sur un nouveau Roméo.

Chapitre X
Tu m'entends, mon cœur?

On a tourné en rond un joli bout de temps. On avait beau se creuser le ciboulot, on n'avait aucune nouvelle idée pour avancer dans notre enquête. On a décidé d'attendre Théo en écoutant de la musique. Elle venait à peine de commencer quand mon cellulaire a sonné.

Au début, la ligne était mauvaise, un peu comme quand Pierre-Yves Hamel m'avait téléphoné, le mois dernier, de sa barrière de corail en Australie. J'ai espéré deux secondes qu'il m'appelait, cette fois de son kayak dans les Laurentides, mais c'est la petite voix claire et douce de tante Alice que j'ai entendue.

— C'est moi, mon poussin. On reprend l'avion pour Montréal dans une heure. Si tout va bien, on sera à la maison avant la noirceur.

Elle a répété trois fois :

— Tu m'entends, mon poussin ?

J'étais trop saisie pour répondre. J'avoue qu'après, j'ai préféré faire semblant de ne pas comprendre. Je n'ai pas dit un mot. J'ai même joué avec les touches du clavier, histoire de simuler une mauvaise réception.

Au bout du fil, j'ai entendu mes tantes se chamailler. C'est tante Béatrice, finalement, qui a pris les choses en main. Elle s'est mise à claironner dans l'appareil :

— On a tellement hâte de te revoir, Rosalie ! On a plein d'histoires à te raconter sur la Gaspésie… la mer et les baleines. Tu m'entends, mon cœur ? Tu m'entends ?

Il y a eu un silence suivi d'un sapristi de mocheté de charabia comme chaque fois que toutes les sept parlent en même temps. J'ai repitonné sur toutes les touches. La communication a fini par couper.

J'ai croisé le regard de Julie.

Avant de me faire rebattre les oreilles, j'ai dit :

— Quoi ! Je ne leur ai pas vraiment claqué la ligne au nez, j'ai seulement fait semblant de ne pas entendre.

Elle a répliqué que c'était du pareil au même. Que j'aurais dû répondre.

J'ai tenté d'expliquer que mes tantes l'avaient mérité. Que je n'étais pas encore prête à leur parler. Que j'avais besoin auparavant de connaître toute la vérité sur ma naissance.

Comme je m'y attendais, mon cellulaire a sonné de nouveau. Julie a sauté sur l'appareil. Elle a pris son ton de maîtresse d'école.

— Allô ! C'est Julie Morin. Terrible comme je vous entends mal… Terrible comme le son est mauvais… Il y a de l'écho, comme si vous étiez plusieurs. Bizarre, maintenant je vous entends mieux.

En fuyant mon regard, elle leur a expliqué que tantôt, c'était elle qui était au téléphone quand tout a flanché. Qu'elle voulait leur dire que ça allait bien. Que je n'étais pas à la maison. Que j'étais partie à la recherche de mon chat. Qu'il avait sauté par la fenêtre du sous-sol, la fenêtre qui donne sur la ruelle. Mais que, juré craché, tout allait bien et pour moi et pour mon chat.

Puis Julie s'est mise à répéter :

— Terrible, je vous entends encore mal… Vous avez quitté Cap-au-Renard ? Vous êtes à l'aéroport de Mont-Joli ? Non… Inutile de rappeler, Rosalie ne sera pas de retour… Oui, elle a hâte de vous revoir, elle aussi. Je le lui dirai, promis, juré... Oui, oui! Bon voyage de retour! Allô... oui!... Allô... Je ne vous entends plus!

Elle m'a déposé le cellulaire dans les mains avant de préciser en se tortillant:

— Bon... oui, j'ai raccroché. Et si j'ai menti, c'est pour la bonne cause. Enfin, je n'ai pas totalement menti, j'ai réorganisé la vérité pour rassurer tes tantes. Bref, tu devrais me remercier.

Finalement, c'est un appel de Théo sur le cellulaire de Julie qui nous a changé les idées. Il avait deux ou trois questions à me poser sur mes parents. Julie m'a tendu l'appareil.

J'ai dû lui avouer à lui aussi que je ne savais presque rien d'eux. Seulement que ma supposée mère s'appelait Anne Brisebois et mon supposé père, François Dansereau. Qu'ils étaient supposément disparus dans un accident d'avion.

Puis, il m'a demandé ma date de naissance. J'ai répondu que j'étais née le 15 juillet. Sous le signe du Cancer. Peut-être à Montréal, en Gaspésie ou dans un quelconque vieux pays.

Théo en a déduit que si l'accident était réel, que si j'étais bien née en juillet, que s'il se fiait à l'allure du bébé sur la photo que Julie lui avait montrée, la tragédie avait eu lieu quelque part en septembre ou en octobre.

Quand j'ai demandé où il voulait en venir, il a laissé tomber :

— Je te le dirai quand j'en saurai plus.

Puis, il a voulu reparler une minute à Julie. Sa minute a duré 14 minutes 23 secondes. Je le sais, j'ai un chrono sur ma montre.

Pour ne pas avoir l'air d'écornifler, je suis revenue vers son ordi et j'ai cliqué de nouveau sur le site *Parents biologiques recherchés*. Je suis restée les yeux dans le vague, à me morfondre jusqu'à ce que la mère de Julie, pour la seconde fois de la fin de semaine, déboule l'escalier du sous-sol en se lamentant.

La pauvre avait les yeux rouges, super enflés, super larmoyants.

J'ai espéré une seconde qu'elle venait d'éplucher des oignons. Mais ce n'était pas la faute aux oignons. C'était bel et bien la faute de Charbon. Par esprit de contradiction, mon sapristi de mocheté de chat avait réussi à se refaufiler dans la maison.

Non seulement madame Morin l'avait entrevu se léchant les babines sur le comptoir de la cuisine, mais quatre minutes plus tard, elle l'avait surpris installé comme un pacha au milieu de son lit. Pour l'instant, elle n'avait aucune idée de l'endroit où il pouvait se cacher. Mais dans l'état où elle se trouvait, Charbon était quelque part dans sa maison et elle nous donnait exactement deux minutes et quart pour le retrouver.

Chapitre XI
Viens, mon bébé !

Pendant une bonne demi-heure, on a cherché Charbon partout. On ne l'a trouvé nulle part. Je veux dire nulle part dans la maison des Morin. C'est beaucoup plus tard que je l'ai aperçu, perché sur la plus haute branche de l'érable qui donne sur le boulevard Saint-Joseph. Le pauvre miaulait comme un perdu.

J'ai répété mille fois : « Viens, Charbon ! Viens, mon bébé ! » Il refusait mordicus de bouger.

La mère de Julie voulait appeler les pompiers. Finalement, c'est monsieur Morin, avec sa plus longue échelle, qui a réussi à le ramener sur le plancher des vaches.

J'ai pris Charbon dans mes bras. J'ai gratouillé sa bedaine. Je voulais le rassurer, lui faire comprendre que pour certaines personnes, son poil causait des malheurs. Comme dans cette maison où on ne voulait pas de lui.

Génial, un chat ! Au lieu de protester, de feuler, de faire le gros dos, il s'est étiré, puis son petit moteur à ronrons est reparti.

J'en ai profité pour demander à Julie de courir au sous-sol récupérer sa litière, ses galettes de poisson, son poteau à griffes et sa souris Mickey. De récupérer aussi mes clés, qui traînaient dans les poches de mon pull à capuche. Que je n'avais

pas le choix, je devais aller barricader Charbon chez moi.

* * *

La maison était super silencieuse. Sans mes tantes, sérieux, les corridors donnaient le cafard. On a grimpé dans ma chambre. On a installé Charbon dans son panier. J'allais redescendre au rez-de-chaussée quand Julie, restée derrière, m'a demandé de venir l'aider.

Je me suis retournée. Elle était en train de décrocher le fameux cadre en disant que ce serait super éclairant de le rapporter, de retirer la photo, de regarder au verso. Qu'après tout, c'était comme ça qu'on avait appris pour Henri Lacasse.

J'ai dit que c'était une sapristi de bonne idée, même si tout le mal qu'on s'était donné ne nous avait rien rapporté.

Cinq minutes plus tard, on revenait chez elle. Dans sa chambre, on a démonté le cadre en vitesse. Avec la loupe, on a inspecté millimètre par millimètre l'arrière de la photo. Il y avait quelque chose d'écrit, mais c'était, cette fois, complètement illisible.

J'ai soupiré :

— … comme si quelqu'un avait fait exprès de l'effacer !

Julie, qui se base toujours sur des indices super solides avant d'affirmer quelque chose, a précisé :

— Je dirais plutôt qu'on a délibérément fait disparaître ce qui était écrit, ou bien le temps s'en est chargé.

À contrecœur, j'ai avoué qu'elle avait peut-être raison, mais que pour moi c'était beaucoup moins nuancé : c'étaient mes tantes qui avaient tout effacé.

* * *

Il était quatre heures pile quand madame Morin nous a demandé de courir au dépanneur. On avait pourtant bien aéré la maison, mais elle voulait, en plus, une canette de sent-bon pour chasser définitivement les odeurs de Charbon. Odeurs qu'elle était la seule à sentir, d'ailleurs.

Julie m'a attrapée par la manche en bougonnant :

— Des fois, je te jure, ma mère est tellement compliquée que j'aimerais ça, être adoptée.

Chapitre XII
L'architecture
et les blocs Lego

Au retour du dépanneur, on a trouvé Théo Bergeron devant la maison. Installé dans les marches, il tapochait sur son portable. Il était si concentré qu'il a sursauté quand Julie a demandé :

— Est-ce qu'on te dérange ?

Il a éclaté de rire, et j'ai remarqué deux fossettes super bien dessinées au milieu de ses joues. Julie s'est assise à côté de lui, collée, collée. Moi, j'ai hésité. J'allais entrer dans la maison quand il a dit :

— Approche…, j'ai quelque chose à te montrer.

Il avait répertorié sur son ordinateur tous les accidents d'avion survenus au Québec. Il y en avait beaucoup. La longue liste a défilé devant mes yeux.

Théo a précisé en s'ébouriffant les cheveux :

Le grand mystère de Rosalie

— Il y en a une cinquantaine. Si au moins j'avais le nom de la compagnie aérienne que tes parents ont utilisée. Ou le type d'avion. Je veux dire… un hélicoptère ? Un bimoteur ou un hydravion ? Un gros 747 ou un mini-Beechcraft ? M'enfin, je ne sais pas moi… quelque chose qui me mettrait sur une piste.

J'ai répondu, excitée :

— J'en ai, une piste ! C'était, selon mes tantes, le PIRE accident aérien que le Québec ait connu.

Théo m'a regardée, navré.

— Je ne voudrais pas te faire de la peine, mais le pire accident aérien que le Québec ait connu s'est produit il y a une quarantaine d'années. C'était à Sainte-Thérèse-de-Blainville. Tu n'étais pas encore née. L'avion était un DC-8, un modèle qui n'existe même plus.

Je me suis retenue de toutes mes forces pour ne pas éclater en sanglots.

Mais sans le vouloir, j'ai senti deux sapristi de mochetés de larmes couler sur mes joues. Je les ai essuyées du revers de la main. Après, j'ai marmonné en reniflant :

— Encore une preuve que mes tantes me racontaient des histoires.

Julie a soupiré :

— Tu connais tes tantes, elles dramatisent toujours. Tes parents ont peut-être disparu dans un tout petit accident. Mais pour elles, c'était comme le plus gros et le pire qui pouvait arriver.

Théo, qui cherchait encore sur son ordi, a annoncé :

— Je pense avoir trouvé autre chose. On parle ici d'une tragédie aérienne survenue dans la ville de Québec.

Il s'est mis à lire à haute voix :

La tragédie impliquait un F-27 de la compagnie Québecair. En route pour Montréal, l'avion s'est écrasé dans un champ après le décollage de l'aéroport Jean-Lesage. L'hélice du moteur droit s'est détachée. Le drame s'est produit à 18 h 45, le 23 juin 1978…

Là, Théo s'est arrêté.

— Avant de lire, j'aurais dû vérifier la date.

J'ai ajouté, le cœur serré :

— On dirait que les pires accidents sont tous survenus dans le temps des dinosaures. D'ailleurs, je me demande à quoi ça sert tout ça ?

Julie a répondu :

— Si on tombe sur le bon accident, je suppose qu'on trouvera tes vrais parents !

Théo a continué :

— … parce qu'on aura la liste des passagers, de l'équipage, donc le nom de toutes les victimes.

J'ai soupiré :

— Ouais ! À la condition qu'Anne Brisebois et François Dansereau aient vraiment existé.

J'étais sur le point d'ajouter quelque chose, mais Julie et Théo se fixaient si intensément, tout à coup, que je me suis presque sentie de trop.

J'allais filer en douce dans la maison quand monsieur Morin est apparu.

— Et le sent-bon de ta mère ? Il semblerait que ça presse !

Julie, troublée, a bondi sur ses pieds. Son père a attrapé la canette. Il a salué Théo et a disparu avec un drôle de sourire. Ce que j'ai fait à mon tour, laissant Julie sur le perron avec son Théo.

Je suis descendue directement au sous-sol ramasser mes traîneries. Je n'avais pas le choix, dans quelques heures je devrais retourner chez mes tantes. Je suis remontée dans la chambre de Julie récupérer les deux cadres avec les photos. J'ai replacé la vitre et vissé les œillets de celui qui était installé dans ma chambre. J'ai même lavé les marques de doigts. Bref, je l'ai remis comme il était.

Ensuite, je suis allée à la cuisine rejoindre la mère de Julie, qui préparait le souper. Pour lui faire plaisir, j'ai dit que maintenant toute sa maison sentait la vraie forêt amazonienne. Puis j'ai proposé, comme ça, d'éplucher ses légumes.

Je me demande si c'est pour se venger qu'elle a déposé un petit couteau pointu et trois énormes oignons jaunes juste devant moi. Si bien que j'avais le regard d'Aurore l'enfant martyre quand Julie s'est remontré le bout du nez. Elle m'a tourné autour avant de me chuchoter à l'oreille :

— C'est peut-être pas le moment, mais Théo aimerait savoir si tes tantes ont déjà raconté que leur frère, je veux dire ton père, avait quelque chose à voir avec l'architecture.

J'ai d'abord répondu non. Mais en y repensant, j'ai précisé que si l'architecture avait quelque chose à voir avec les blocs Lego, c'était oui.

J'ai expliqué qu'il y a longtemps, quand j'étais toute petite et que je m'amusais des heures avec des piles de blocs, j'ai entendu une de mes tantes dire quelque chose comme :

— Trouvez pas qu'elle est aussi habile que son père pour construire des machins en trois dimensions ?

Julie, qui jubilait, est disparue pop! comme par magie. Sa mère m'a jeté un drôle de regard… comme si quelque chose de super important lui avait échappé. J'aurais dû tourner ma langue trente-deux fois avant de déclarer:

— Je ne comprends plus rien à Julie quand SON beau Théo traîne aux alentours!

Elle a dit:

— Qui ça, SON beau Théo?

J'ai bredouillé:

— Bien… celui qui est avec elle sur la galerie. Il vient de Québec.

Madame Morin a foncé tout droit vers la galerie. Par chance, il n'y avait plus personne sur le perron quand elle est arrivée. N'empêche que sitôt le retour de Julie, sa mère n'a pu s'empêcher de lui poser des dizaines de questions.

Julie m'a regardée, écœurée. Je ne lui ai pas laissé le temps de s'offusquer, je lui ai soufflé à l'oreille:

— Si ça ne te fait rien, je préfère qu'on descende au sous-sol pour en parler.

Pendant que sa mère, une patte en l'air, nous annonçait qu'il nous restait à peine cinquante minutes avant le souper, on déboulait l'escalier.

Heureusement que ma meilleure amie est en amour par-dessus la tête. Finalement, malgré mon indiscrétion, tout s'est arrangé.

Chapitre XIII
Un certain courage

Immédiatement après le souper, Théo a téléphoné pour nous annoncer qu'il était presque convaincu d'avoir trouvé ce qu'on cherchait. Qu'il arrivait dans la minute pour nous le montrer.

On s'est installés tous les trois dans le sous-sol. Avant d'ouvrir son ordi, Théo a voulu me prévenir :

— Ce que tu vas voir est assez éprouvant. Je dirais même qu'il te faudra un certain courage.

J'allais répondre par une insignifiance, mais j'ai cru préférable de me taire.

Il a continué :

— Bien… voici ce que j'ai d'abord découvert sur le site des archives d'un journal de Québec.

À l'écran, une image est apparue. Une image en noir et blanc. Une image sombre, assez sinistre, bref, pas rigolote du tout. On y voyait les débris encore fumants d'un avion. Des débris qui jonchaient le sol sur une assez grande distance. En m'approchant, j'ai discerné une hélice, de la tôle tordue, deux moteurs éventrés. Le cœur m'a manqué.

Théo a murmuré :

— C'est ce qui restait du Cessna 425 le lendemain de l'accident.

J'ai dit, une boule dans la gorge :

— Tu ne me dis pas ça pour rien ?

Il a répondu non. Que c'était bel et bien l'avion dans lequel mon père et ma mère avaient disparu.

J'ai demandé, troublée :

— Comment tu le sais ?

— Bien… dans l'article de journal, on parle des cinq passagers qui ont péri dans la tragédie. Plus particulièrement des deux jeunes architectes François Dansereau et Anne Brisebois. On dit qu'ils devaient se rendre à Havre-Saint-Pierre via Sept-Îles pour présenter les plans de la future école qu'ils avaient dessinés.

Des larmes terriblement chaudes ont commencé à couler sur mes joues.

Théo a précisé qu'il y avait autre chose. Il a cliqué de nouveau sur l'écran et la page suivante du journal est apparue. Il a dit :

— C'est une courte entrevue que tes parents ont donnée à ce journal quelques minutes avant leur départ pour Sept-Îles. Pas qu'ils étaient des vedettes, mais leur projet était super important pour les autochtones de la Côte-Nord. J'ai déjà imprimé la page. Tu pourras la lire quand tu voudras.

Fascinée, les jambes en guenilles, je n'écoutais plus, je fixais l'écran. Ou plutôt, je fixais le bébé qui, entre ses parents, mâchouillait sa suce en souriant.

J'ai entendu Julie dire à Théo :

— … presque la même photo que celle installée sur le mur de sa chambre.

J'ai pris la feuille que Théo avait imprimée et, tranquillement, je suis allée me retirer dans le coin le plus reculé, le plus secret du sous-sol.

Les yeux rivés sur la photo, j'ai pris une éternité avant de lire la légende écrite dessous. Une sapristi de mocheté de légende avec des mots qui m'ont écrabouillé le cœur. Pourtant, c'était seulement écrit :

Le grand mystère de Rosalie

Quelques minutes avant leur départ, on peut voir Anne Brisebois et François Dansereau avec, dans leurs bras, leur petite fille Rosalie.

Je me suis mise à pleurer. J'ai pleuré longtemps, longtemps, longtemps.

* * *

Quand j'ai repris mes esprits, Théo était parti et j'ai pu lire sans renifler l'article dans lequel mes parents expliquaient leur projet. Un projet plein de respect, de trouvailles et d'imagination, comme on disait dans le journal. J'ai vu aussi les mots « Henri Lacasse, photographe », imprimés sur le côté de la photo.

Plus tard, Julie s'est approchée de moi sur la pointe des pieds. Elle a dit, émue :

— N'empêche qu'à trois, on a réussi à éclaircir un grand mystère… Et tu n'as plus à douter maintenant…, tu es une véritable Dansereau.

J'ai hoché la tête et j'ai souri.

À huit heures moins le quart, j'étais déjà dans le vestibule des Morin à attendre, excitée, le retour de mes tantes. Je tenais d'une main mes deux DVD et mes patins à roues alignées. De l'autre, mon sac à dos avec à l'intérieur la coupure de journal glissée précieusement entre les deux cadres.

Impatiente, je trépignais depuis une bonne demi-heure, le nez collé à la vitre, quand mon cellulaire a sonné. C'était tante Diane m'avertissant qu'elles étaient arrivées saines et sauves à l'aéroport de Montréal.

J'ai poussé un super « youpi ! » avant de les prévenir de ne pas venir me prendre chez Julie, que je partais illico pour la maison. Que mon chat, sa litière, son poteau à griffes, ses galettes de poisson et sa souris Mickey étaient déjà rendus.

Après, j'ai dit mille fois merci aux Morin, serré très fort mon amie Julie, avant de bondir comme un chien fou vers la maison.

Chapitre XIV
Enfin des réponses !

J'avais tellement hâte de leur sauter au cou ! Mais quand je les ai vues descendre de leur fourgonnette, j'ai fait un effort terrible pour ne pas courir me cacher. Comme si toutes mes sapristi de mochetés de fausses accusations de la fin de semaine pouvaient se lire sur mon front.

J'étais mal à l'aise quand elles m'ont embrassée en répétant combien elles s'étaient ennuyées. Encore plus quand elles ont aperçu, sur la table de la cuisine, les deux cadres avec la coupure de journal que j'avais cru bon d'étaler.

Elles se sont arrêtées net de rire. Je pense même qu'elles ont rougi toutes les sept, avant de blêmir.

C'est moi qui ai rompu le silence.

— Ne vous en faites pas, je suis assez grande maintenant pour connaître la vérité.

Tante Béatrice a précisé qu'elles m'avaient toujours dit toute la vérité. Toujours répété que mes parents étaient disparus dans un accident d'avion et qu'ils étaient quelque part dans leur ciel avec les anges.

J'ai répondu que c'était une vérité pour me rassurer. Mais qu'à douze ans, j'avais senti le besoin d'en savoir davantage.

Elles se sont assises autour de la table. La coupure de journal circulait d'une main à l'autre. Et sans exagérer, on pouvait entendre une mouche voler. Curieusement, on sentait aussi dans l'air un immense soulagement. Comme si depuis toujours, pour me ménager, mes tantes avaient évité de parler de leur frère adoré.

J'ai dit en baissant les yeux :

— J'ai beaucoup de questions à vous poser. Pour commencer, j'aimerais savoir qui c'était, ce Rosaire-Timothée ? Je veux dire par rapport à la famille Dansereau ?

C'est tante Béatrice qui a répondu.

— Ce Rosaire-Timothée, mon cœur, était le dernier Dansereau encore installé en Gaspésie. C'était le frère de ton grand-père. À l'époque, il pêchait la morue sur un chalutier qu'il avait baptisé *La Vieille Picouille*. On n'a jamais su pourquoi.

Tout le monde a éclaté de rire. D'un coup, l'atmosphère s'est détendue.

Petit à petit, j'ai appris qu'après la naissance de mon père, le seul garçon de la famille, mes grands-parents avaient quitté Cap-au-Renard pour s'installer à Québec. Qu'après des études en architecture à l'Université Laval, mon père avait rencontré Anne Brisebois, ma mère, à Florence en Italie.

Tante Diane, rêveuse, a soupiré, la main sur le coeur :

— C'était, mon ange, une ville merveilleuse pour deux amoureux de l'architecture comme eux. Quelques mois après, ils se sont mariés à Grenoble, la ville natale de ta mère, avant de revenir à Québec pour s'y installer.

Tante Colette a ajouté en fronçant les sourcils :

— Ç'a été un véritable coup de foudre entre les deux. Un amour comme on n'en avait jamais vu. Tu comprends ça, ma soie.

Là, elles se sont mises à parler toutes en même temps pour dire combien l'accident avait été terrible et injuste. Que par chance, ce jour-là, mes parents avaient eu la bonne idée de leur confier leur trésor. Comme s'ils avaient eu une sorte de pressentiment.

C'est pour ça qu'après la catastrophe, mes sept tantes avaient voulu prendre soin ensemble de la petite orpheline que j'étais devenue.

Quelques mois après, elles ont décidé d'aller vivre à Montréal dans la grande maison du boulevard Saint-Joseph. Elles pensaient qu'à sept, ce serait plus facile de me choyer et moins difficile de faire mon éducation.

J'ai appris aussi que ma mère parlait français avec un petit accent du sud de la France. Que j'avais un nez pointu comme le sien. Que mes tantes n'avaient pas eu beaucoup de temps pour la connaître, mais que son imagination débordante et son exubérance les avaient fascinées.

J'ai dit comme ça :

— C'est d'elle finalement que j'ai hérité de mon sapristi de mocheté de penchant pour le drame et l'exagération.

Personne n'a osé nier. Seule tante Alice a précisé :

— C'est parce que des fois, mon poussin, tu t'emballes trop facilement.

Après, elles ont parlé de mon père, leur frère. Et ma foi, il n'y a pas une seule super belle qualité contenue dans le dictionnaire qu'elles n'ont pas utilisée. J'ai compris combien elles l'avaient aimé.

* * *

Ce soir-là, pour m'endormir, j'avais Charbon installé sur mes pieds et la coupure du journal de Québec sous mon oreiller. J'avais aussi, accrochées sur le mur au-dessus de mon lit, les deux photos presque identiques de Rosalie Dansereau entre Anne Brisebois, sa maman, et François Dansereau, son papa.

Je savais maintenant que mes tantes avaient reçu l'une d'elles par la poste. C'était quelques jours après l'accident. Il n'y avait ni mot ni rien. Que la photo, avec écrit derrière : *Henri Lacasse, photographe.*

Chapitre XV
Belle comme un cœur

Le lendemain, j'avais bien des choses à raconter à ma meilleure amie. Bien des choses à raconter aussi à Pierre-Yves Hamel. Même que j'avais envie de les révéler au monde entier.

Mais celui que je considérais encore comme mon amoureux n'était pas à l'école. Je n'arrivais à le joindre ni au téléphone ni à la maison. Comme si toute la famille Hamel avait disparu d'un coup.

Ce n'est qu'à six heures du soir que madame sa mère a répondu au téléphone. Elle a dit, un tantinet impatiente comme d'habitude :

— Je suis très étonnée, ma petite Rosalie… Pierre-Yves aurait dû te dire qu'il restait deux journées de plus au lac Vert, dans les

Laurentides. C'est pour terminer son stage en canoë-kayak.

Et comme exprès pour me bouleverser :

— Il a oublié son cellulaire, mais tu pourrais le joindre chez une certaine Josée Bélanger, une copine. Pour l'occasion, ses parents ont eu la gentillesse de l'héberger. Josée fait son stage avec lui. Elle est jolie comme un cœur et elle habite près d'un lac juste à côté.

D'un coup, la terre a cessé de tourner, j'ai bafouillé :

— … un stage… avec une copine… belle comme…

Enfin, j'ai noté le numéro de téléphone et j'ai raccroché. Après, j'ai hésité entre appeler Pierre-Yves pour lui dire ma façon de penser ou me rabattre sur ma meilleure amie.

J'ai décidé de téléphoner à Julie. Quand elle a répondu, j'ai lancé d'une traite :

— Tu sais comme j'haïs l'eau. Tu sais que je nage comme un marteau. Ce que tu ne sais pas, Julie Morin, c'est que mon supposé chum est probablement en train de me tromper avec une sapristi de mocheté de pro du canoë-kayak, belle comme un cœur et qui doit nager comme la sirène de Disney.

Et partagée entre la colère et les larmes, j'ai demandé :

— Je fais quoi, moi ? J'avais tellement de choses importantes à lui raconter sur mon père et sur ma mère.

Évidemment, ma meilleure amie m'a répété pour la millième fois que je m'en faisais pour rien. Que j'exagérais encore. Que je devais attendre avant de grimper dans les rideaux. Et pour me changer les idées, elle a lancé en pouffant de rire :

— Tu ne devineras jamais! J'ai, paraît-il, à Warwick, une arrière-grand-tante nommée Albina-Églantine Morin qui vient de fêter ses 106 ans.

J'ai demandé:

— C'est quoi le rapport?

Elle a répondu qu'il n'y en avait pas, mais que sa sœur Désirée-Amanda… Et là, je l'ai coupée sec en lui signifiant que je ne lui avais pas téléphoné pour parler de vieilles tantes qui voyageaient à dos de *tyrannosaurus rex*. Que c'était pour parler de Pierre-Yves et de cette Josée Bélanger. Que je n'avais aucune sapristi de mocheté d'envie de rire. Que je vivais peut-être ma première vraie peine d'amour. Que j'avais le cœur en mille morceaux. Que cette Josée ne perdait rien pour attendre. Que j'allais me défendre.

Elle a riposté:

— Tu ne vas pas capoter comme Marie-Ève Poirier et lui envoyer des courriels anonymes?

J'ai dit:

— C'est pas l'envie qui manque!

Toujours pour me changer les idées, elle m'a parlé de son Théo. Ça ne m'a pas aidée à me calmer. Pire, quand j'ai raccroché, je suis allée chialer devant la télé. Je voulais retrouver mon sang-froid. Ç'a été plus fort que moi. Après dix minutes, j'ai foncé sur mon ordi.

Par curiosité, j'ai cherché si quelqu'un avait finalement fondé le fameux site des *Ex-trompées du beau Théo Bergeron*. Évidemment, je n'ai rien trouvé parce que Marie-Ève avait tout inventé.

C'est en me rongeant les sangs comme une idiote que j'ai eu la super bonne idée de créer, pour de vrai, un blogue exprès pour les désespérés. Le blogue le plus super utile depuis l'invention d'internet. Un blogue que n'importe quelle sapristi de mocheté d'âme en peine sur la planète pourrait utiliser. Il lui suffirait de cliquer sur : http://mapremierepeinedamour.ca. Enfin... quelque chose comme ça. De toute façon, j'aurais Julie Morin et Théo Bergeron, deux super-cracs en informatique, pour me conseiller. Et peut-être Pierre-Yves Hamel si jamais, avec cette Josée Bélanger, je m'étais encore fait des idées.

Épilogue

Au retour de Pierre-Yves, mardi soir à dix-sept heures pile, j'ai su que pour la première fois de sa vie Julie Morin s'était trompée. Je n'avais pas exagéré, Pierre-Yves Hamel n'était plus mon amoureux. Je lui ai même remis son coton ouaté et sa montre Swatch. J'ai gardé le petit cœur turquoise qu'il m'avait donné pour fêter l'anniversaire de notre premier baiser. Il dit qu'on sera toujours amis.

Pour l'instant, je n'arrive pas à l'imaginer autrement que nageant avec sa sirène dans les Laurentides. Ça me fait beaucoup pleurer. C'est si triste de penser qu'il ne sera plus mon grand héros viking.

N'empêche, avec Théo et Julie, je l'ai créé, mon fameux blogue http://mapremierepeinedamour.ca. Il existe depuis à peine deux semaines, et on a déjà reçu dix-sept textes super beaux et super émouvants. Je me dis que c'est important de savoir qu'on n'est pas tout seul quand cette sapristi de mocheté de catastrophe nous arrive.

· Julie et Théo pensent fournir une trousse de secours super efficace pour remonter le moral de nos correspondants. Ils ont déjà une liste longue comme le bras de trucs super comiques pour leur changer les idées.

Moi, pour l'instant, je n'ai pas la tête à la rigolade. Par chance, je les ai tous les deux pour m'écouter. J'ai aussi mes tantes, et aussi mon vrai père et ma vraie mère dans leur ciel.

J'oubliais : hier, Julie m'a raconté que c'était la première semaine que Marie-Ève ne lui avait pas envoyé, par courriel, une de ses niaiseries. Plus tard, on a su par Marco Tifo qu'elle avait un nouvel amoureux. C'est exactement ce qu'on avait prédit.

Enfin, Julie a fini par me dire la chose si personnelle que Théo lui avait chuchotée à l'oreille. En fait, je l'avais presque devinée, mais j'ai promis de ne pas la révéler.

Table des matières

Au magasin photo, Rosalie découvre une photo d'elle et de ses parents. À part quelques détails, on jurerait la réplique de celle qui orne le mur de sa chambre ! Comment est-ce possible ? Rosalie se met à douter du décès de ses parents et son imagination part en vrille. Une chance que sa fidèle amie Julie est là pour lui ramener les pieds sur terre et l'aider à résoudre ce mystère !

Lorenzo

KJ-312-720

Illustrations. Marisol Sarrazin

ISBN 978-2-

WILLIAM SHAKESPEARE
(From the engraving in the First Folio)

A similar thought comes into Hamlet's mind at a tragic moment. He is about—so he thinks—to slay his uncle, and he remembers the death of his own father :

> " He took my father grossly full of bread."

Obviously " bread " had an unpleasant significance for Shakespeare. It throws an unexpected sidelight on his digestion and Mrs. Shakespeare's cooking ; but this is perhaps a frivolous way of looking at the problem.

Professor Spurgeon's method is to card-index, analyse and tabulate all Shakespeare's images, and, as part of the process, to analyse the imagery used by other Elizabethan dramatists. The result is to confirm certain impressions : that Shakespeare has far more images drawn from sport than other dramatists, that Marlowe's imagery is predominantly drawn from the classics, and so forth. It is a fascinating pastime, and one of the few forms of literary research that can be carried out at home. One requires only a volume of Shakespeare's plays and a number of cards for the card-index.

The values and limitations of this kind of study lie in its being mechanical ; an absolutely mechanical scientific collection of statistics of this kind reveals much of the processes of the human mind which would escape notice altogether in ordinary reading. It cannot be carried too far, for a poetic image is not a simple or mechanical expression, but, especially in Shakespeare's later period, a fusion of all kinds of sparkling ideas. It is often quite impossible to separate the particular images in a clot of imagery such as :

> " Come thick Night,
> And pall thee in the dunnest smoke of Hell,
> That my keen knife see not the wound it makes,
> Nor Heaven peep through the blanket of the dark,
> To cry, hold, hold."

In this passage neither knife nor blanket can suitably be classified under " Images drawn from domestic articles."

Nevertheless, within reason, a study of imagery will give results similar to chemical analysis. The water of a well, when analysed, will show so much of this, so much of that, and perhaps a minute trace of zinc. The analysis is entirely objective ; it is not the business of the chemist to say how zinc should be present in the water. The history of the well will show that some six months before, a bucket had accidentally been dropped in. A study of Shakespeare's imagery will show many of his experiences, but not how and when he came by them.

Occasionally, when the material exists, it is possible to trace the actual source of a poetic image. Professor J. Livingstone Lowes studied Coleridge's Kubla Khan and The Ancient Mariner. He had as external evidence Coleridge's notebooks, which showed what Coleridge had been reading at the time. Moreover, from Dorothy Wordsworth's *Journals* and similar sources Coleridge's external experiences were recorded. As a result, in *The Road to Xanadu*, Professor Lowes was able to trace back almost every idea and phrase in *Kubla Khan* and *The Ancient Mariner* to its original source, and thereby to present a fascinating picture of how the poet's mind worked. Similarly, by comparing Keats' letters and his poetry, Mr. Middleton Murry was able to show how Keats' mind worked.

Unfortunately there are no notebooks for Shakespeare, and any deductions must be largely guesswork. One cannot even tell whether an image is negative or positive. A man may be full of images of sport either because he is himself a great sportsman, or because he is feeble-bodied and envies those of better physique. Sporting journalists are not necessarily expert sportsmen. Nor are those who make a particular study of Shakespeare's imagery agreed amongst themselves.

Once, having a private theory of my own, based on the fact that Shakespeare's images drawn from the sea and war indicated that at some time or other he had seen war and the sea at first hand, I put it to two authorities on Shakespearian imagery. I asked each of them the same question : " Do you, from your intensive study of Shakespeare's imagery, gather that he had personal experience of the sea ? " The one replied, " Of course " ; and the other, " Certainly not."

From this one can deduce that, just as a poetic image comes from a poet's experience, which includes the books that he has read, so also the perception of an image and of its significance by readers or hearers comes from their experience. Unless the critic has had the same range of experiences as the author he will miss many images and their significance. As Keats put it in a letter, when writing of Wordsworth, " We find what he says true as far as we have experienced, and we can judge no further but by larger experience—for axioms in philosophy are not axioms until they are proved upon our pulses. We read fine things, but never feel them to the full until we have gone the same steps as the author.— I know this is not plain ; you will know exactly my meaning when I say that now I shall relish Hamlet more than I have ever done."

Here again, scholarship is important, for until the reader himself has some knowledge of Elizabethan idiom—and this requires a considerable knowledge of the Elizabethan background—he cannot appreciate the full meaning of many Elizabethan images. Macbeth, for instance, returning from the murder of Duncan with his hands covered with blood, and dazed with horror at what he has seen and done, murmurs :

" One cried God bless us, and Amen the other,
    As they had seen me with these hangman's hands."

To a modern reader there is no reason why a hang-man should not have clean hands ; it would show a lack of delicacy for him to exercise his profession unwashed. But to Shakespeare's audience the phrase had a ghastly significance, for in executions for treason it was the hangman's business to tear out the victim's entrails before hacking the body into quarters.

Again, such a phrase as " on your allegiance " or " on your peril " means very little to a modern reader. If used in official documents which retain ancient formulas, it means little more than " other-wise you will be liable to a penalty not exceeding £5." To an Elizabethan " on your allegiance " was the solemnest form of command ; to disobey it was to commit high treason and to risk the ghastly penalty.

iv

The third approach is the dramatic. Just as critical and scholarly notions about Shakespeare have changed in the last thirty years, so also has the fashion of producing his plays in the modern theatre. Sir Henry Irving died in 1905. He was the great leader of one school of Shakespearian presentation, magnificent, gorgeous and elaborate. The produc-tions of Sir Herbert Beerbohm Tree in the years before the war were even more spectacular, and are still talked of by theatre-goers of the older genera-tion. It is a sign of complete change of taste that

Tree's expensive realism is nowadays regarded as ridiculous. When, about twelve years ago, A Midsummer Night's Dream was produced on this scale at Drury Lane, and when more recently Julius Caesar was acted in the Tree manner, critics derided the productions. Tree took realism too far. Real rabbits are not necessary to create the atmosphere for A Midsummer Night's Dream, nor are fountains of real water with real goldfish necessary for Antony and Cleopatra. To import such paraphernalia into Shakespearian production is to regard Shakespeare as matter requiring illustration. Moreover, to give time for the scenery to be set, the plays themselves had to be cut, altered and rearranged. And indeed, thirty years ago, except for such enthusiasts as the late William Poel, Shakespeare's plays were regarded as in themselves unactable.

It was not until the Granville-Barker productions at the Savoy Theatre (1911–13) that it was generally realised that Shakespeare really knew how to make plays, that elaborate decoration is not wanted, and that the little scenes in his plays are important.

The modern theory of Shakespearian production is that Shakespeare's plays must be played as they were written, and as they were intended to be played, entire, rapidly, without pauses. In this way the work of modern scholars and critics has influenced stage production. This was seen in such a production as Mr. John Gielgud's Romeo and Juliet, when the scenery, though attractive and full of colour, was deliberately constructed to give rapid playing. Thus the whole play was preserved and acted at great speed, with the result that the production revealed how magnificent is the plot of Romeo and Juliet, apart altogether from its poetry.

For the student, whether critic, scholar or actor, all three approaches meet in Dr. Harley Granville-Barker's Prefaces to Shakespeare, which are the most stimulating and illuminating criticisms of Shakespeare that have appeared in the last thirty years.

CHAPTER IV

SHAKESPEARE'S COMPANY

THE company of players known first as the Lord Chamberlain's Players, and later as the King's Men, came into existence in the summer of 1594. There had been severe outbreaks of the plague in 1592 and 1593, and at such times the London playhouses were closed. The companies were badly disorganised by these continual interruptions. When at last playing could be resumed in London, there was a considerable regrouping. Edward Alleyn, now at the peak of his fame as an actor of tragedy parts, formed a new company under the patronage of the Lord Admiral, which opened at the Rose Theatre on the Bankside south of London Bridge. A few weeks later a new Lord Chamberlain's Company began to play at the Theatre at Shoreditch, north of the city. This playhouse was owned by James Burbage.

The Theatre had been built in 1576. In the 1570's there had been much friction between the playing companies and the Lord Mayor and Aldermen of the City of London. Hitherto, players had acted to the public in various City inns. It was not a desirable arrangement, and the City authorities did their utmost to prevent it. The objections to plays were those perpetual to any form of public entertainment which attracts rowdy crowds. Not only were there riots and disturbances from time to time, but the players sometimes indulged in unseemly comment on their betters, and, above all, there was a perpetual risk of the plague, which was easily spread in crowded assemblies. The Lord Mayor succeeded in preventing the players from acting within the jurisdiction of the City. The boundaries of the City, however, were small, and London was already spreading out well beyond its limits. To the north in the Middlesex suburbs, and south of the river in the Surrey suburbs, the jurisdiction lay with the Magistrates of Middlesex and Surrey, who were far more complacent.

In 1576 James Burbage acquired a twenty-one years' lease of a piece of land in Shoreditch, and there erected the first permanent playhouse, which was named the Theatre. The venture was a success. Other playhouses followed. By 1594 there were also the Curtain in the Shoreditch neighbourhood, and the Rose on the Bankside, the suburb which had grown up at the south end of London Bridge.

James Burbage had originally been chief player of the great Earl of Leicester. His son, Richard Burbage, was now making a name for himself as a tragic actor. He had learnt his business under Alleyn, but they parted company; and now, in the autumn of 1594, Richard Burbage became the leader of a new Lord Chamberlain's Company. This Company also included Will Kemp, and Shakespeare. William Kemp in his own way was as famous as Alleyn. He was the clown of the Company. He had already played considerably on the Continent. His style of acting, to which there are a number of references, was broad : he was a low comedian, and he preferred to have the stage to himself so that he might amuse the people by his own crude and at times gross antics. Kemp was particularly famous for jigs. At this time it was still the fashion to end the afternoon's entertainment with a jig, which was a short song and dance with one or two characters miming some simple (and usually bawdy) tale.

Between 1592 and 1593 both Marlowe and Greene, hitherto the only English writers to make much name for themselves on the public stages, had died. Kyd, the author of the famous *Spanish Tragedy*, died before the end of 1594. Thus, for a few months, the Chamberlain's Men had a great advantage in Shakespeare, who was the only dramatist with any considerable reputation.

By 1594 Shakespeare had already written three parts of *Henry VI*, and *Richard III*, which told the story of the beginnings of the Wars of the Roses, and their final end, when Henry Tudor defeated Richard III at the Battle of Bosworth Field, *Titus Andronicus*, *The Two Gentlemen of Verona*, *Love's*

Labour's Lost, The Taming of the Shrew, and the *Comedy of Errors.*

The Lord Chamberlain's Company acted the *Comedy of Errors* at Christmas, 1594, as part of the elaborate revels of Gray's Inn at Court. One of their earliest successes was *Romeo and Juliet,* which perfectly accorded with the mood of the moment for sonneteering and love poetry. Soon afterwards Shakespeare wrote *A Midsummer Night's Dream,* apparently for some special performance at a wedding, and about 1595 he continued the story of the troubles of the 15th century, by showing how they all began when Richard II was unlawfully deposed, and afterwards murdered by his cousin, Henry Bolingbroke, thereby bringing down the curse upon the House of Lancaster which was the theme of the plays of the Wars of the Roses. *King John* and *The Merchant of Venice* were written probably in 1596.

Shakespeare had certainly prospered in these months. The application for the Coat of Arms made in his father's name in 1596 shows that the family considered itself sufficiently well-to-do to claim the right to be officially recognised as gentlefolk. The Coat was granted by the Heralds, and the motto chosen was significant—" Non sanz droict " ; what history lies behind this self-conscious challenge is not known, though much can be guessed.

There was trouble for Shakespeare in this year, 1596, though the details are regrettably brief. In

1931 Professor Leslie Hotson published his discovery of a new reference to Shakespeare. It is a record that William Wayt claimed sureties of the peace against William Shakespeare, Francis Langley, Dorothy Soer and Ann Lee, for fear of death, and so forth. Unfortunately nothing is definitely known of the cause of William Wayt's anxiety.

The Company also had its disappointments in 1596. James Burbage, who in his own way had a touch of genius, realised that conditions in the playgoing world were changing. In 1580 men of taste and education had little good to say of the theatres. Sir Philip Sidney, in his *Apology for Poetry*, had condemned them heartily for their lack of propriety. Now, however, that good writers had been attracted to write plays, young men of fashion and intelligence were becoming interested in the theatres. Burbage saw that they, rather than the general public, were the most paying patrons of the theatre. But gentlemen of taste were put off by the mixed and noisy crowds who paid their pennies to stand in the yard of the public playhouse. Some few years before, a very successful private theatre had existed for a few years in the Blackfriars. It had been managed by John Lyly and the actors were choir boys from St. Paul's and the Chapel Royal. Lyly's venture had come to an end about 1590. While it lasted it catered solely for a better-class audience.

The lease of the ground on which the Theatre

stood was coming to an end, and James Burbage thought to revive the idea of the private theatre. Plays in the public theatres were acted in the open air. A private indoor theatre would not be affected by the weather, and it was better to attract a small audience paying good prices than a larger audience paying their pennies. He therefore acquired the refectory of the old Blackfriars Monastery—the site is now occupied by The Times building—and proceeded at considerable expense to turn it into an indoor playhouse.

Blackfriars at this time was a fashionable residential quarter. The aristocratic inhabitants complained that the playhouse would be a great nuisance with its noises of drums and trumpets, and its crowds of people. Accordingly the Privy Council gave orders that Burbage was not to use the building for playing, and the venture was for a long time a complete loss.

The year 1597 also was full of anxiety for the Lord Chamberlain's Men. The lease of the ground upon which the Theatre stood had originally been taken out for twenty-one years. It expired in April 1597. By the conditions of the lease, either Burb— could renew the lease on agreed terms, or he —st remove the playhouse building before its e—. If he did not fulfil these conditions the—d, a man called appropriated to the ground —ifficult. He knew Giles Alleyn. Alleyn p— rebuild their theatre, that the players did n—

but he refused to offer terms which were in any way acceptable. The wrangle continued for many months.

Meanwhile, on 28th July, 1597, all theatres were peremptorily shut by order of the Privy Council. The trouble arose through the Earl of Pembroke's players, who were playing at the Swan (a new playhouse erected on the Bankside) and put on a play called *The Isle of Dogs*. It was a very seditious and topical comedy, and its authors were Thomas Nashe and Ben Jonson. Jonson at this time was an actor in Pembroke's Company. The Privy Council were so angry that they ordered playing to cease forthwith, and Jonson and two fellow-actors, Gabriel Spencer and Robert Shaa, were put in prison. There was no further playing until the autumn.

Meanwhile, Shakespeare had gained new notoriety. For some reason, which does not seem quite obvious nowadays, the subjects of Queen Elizabeth in the 1590's found certain close parallels between the political situation in the reign of Richard II and in their own times. It was never safe to make direct comment on current affairs, but historical plays and books which seemed to offer oblique political criticism were ually popular. Somehow it was felt that Queen abeth resembled Richard II, and many of the fo ts of the Earl of Essex, who was now beginning out of favour, saw in him a second Bolingbrok

stood was coming to an end, and James Burbage thought to revive the idea of the private theatre. Plays in the public theatres were acted in the open air. A private indoor theatre would not be affected by the weather, and it was better to attract a small audience paying good prices than a larger audience paying their pennies. He therefore acquired the refectory of the old Blackfriars Monastery—the site is now occupied by The Times building—and proceeded at considerable expense to turn it into an indoor playhouse.

Blackfriars at this time was a fashionable residential quarter. The aristocratic inhabitants complained that the playhouse would be a great nuisance with its noises of drums and trumpets, and its crowds of people. Accordingly the Privy Council gave orders that Burbage was not to use the building for playing, and the venture was for a long time a complete loss.

The year 1597 also was full of anxiety for the Lord Chamberlain's Men. The lease of the ground upon which the Theatre stood had originally been taken out for twenty-one years. It expired in April 1597. By the conditions of the lease, either Burbage could renew the lease on agreed terms, or he must remove the playhouse building before its expiry. If he did not fulfil these conditions then the building was appropriated to the ground landlord, a man called Giles Alleyn. Alleyn proved difficult. He knew that the players did not wish to rebuild their theatre,

but he refused to offer terms which were in any way acceptable. The wrangle continued for many months.

Meanwhile, on 28th July, 1597, all theatres were peremptorily shut by order of the Privy Council. The trouble arose through the Earl of Pembroke's players, who were playing at the Swan (a new play-house erected on the Bankside) and put on a play called *The Isle of Dogs*. It was a very seditious and topical comedy, and its authors were Thomas Nashe and Ben Jonson. Jonson at this time was an actor in Pembroke's Company. The Privy Council were so angry that they ordered playing to cease forthwith, and Jonson and two fellow-actors, Gabriel Spencer and Robert Shaa, were put in prison. There was no further playing until the autumn.

Meanwhile, Shakespeare had gained new notoriety. For some reason, which does not seem quite obvious nowadays, the subjects of Queen Elizabeth in the 1590's found certain close parallels between the political situation in the reign of Richard II and in their own times. It was never safe to make direct comment on current affairs, but historical plays and books which seemed to offer oblique political criti-cism were usually popular. Somehow it was felt that Queen Elizabeth resembled Richard II, and many of the followers of the Earl of Essex, who was now beginning to fall out of favour, saw in him a second Bolingbroke.

In August 1597 Andrew Wise printed Shakespeare's *Richard II*. It was a most popular publication, and in six months went into three editions. The play, however, was not complete, for the deposition scene was left out.

About this time, Shakespeare began to write the sequel to *Richard II* in the first part of *Henry IV*. It was another stage in the story of the curse on the House of Lancaster. Naturally, any story about Henry introduced his madcap son Prince Hal, who was a popular and legendary hero. He had already appeared on the stage in an old play called *The Famous Victory of Henry V*, where his companion in mischief was called Sir John Oldcastle. When Shakespeare wrote the play in the autumn of 1597, London was swarming with captains who had returned with Essex from the expedition known as the Islands Voyage. One of these Shakespeare began to envisage as Prince Hal's companion. He called him Sir John Oldcastle. This caused trouble. The real Sir John Oldcastle was burnt for his Lollard principles during the reign of Henry V, and therefore secured his place in *Foxe's Book of Martyrs*. Oldcastle was known also as Lord Cobham, and the Lord Cobham of Shakespeare's day, an unpleasant young man who had just succeeded to the title, objected. Shakespeare was obliged, therefore, to alter the name of Oldcastle, who henceforward became Falstaff.

In this play, too, he parodied one of his own

most effective scenes. In the passage where the Prodigal Prince rehearses his interview with his father, Shakespeare made Falstaff play the stage King " in Cambyses' vein." It was an obvious and broad parody of the style and acting of Edward Alleyn. The parody was successful. Shakespeare followed the first part of *Henry IV* with a Second Part, into which he introduced a new character, Ancient Pistol, who stalked about the stage, strutting and behaving in Alleyn's manner in a vocabulary which was largely composed of ranting misquotations from plays in the repertory of the Admiral's Men.

The year 1598 was exciting in many ways for the Lord Chamberlain's Company. Falstaff from the very first was a great success. Then in the early autumn the Company put on a play by a new author who was beginning to make his name. Ben Jonson, after his imprisonment over the *Isle of Dogs* affair, had joined the Lord Admiral's Men and was writing plays for them ; but for some reason he quarrelled with the Admiral's Men, with the result that his first good play, *Every Man in His Humour*, was offered to the Chamberlain's Men. They acted it in September with considerable success. The play had a sensational advertisement. Gabriel Spencer, who had been Jonson's companion in misfortune over the *Isle of Dogs*, waited for Jonson as he was coming from the playhouse and quarrelled with him. The two men fought each other in Hoxton Fields, and Spencer was killed. Jonson was again put in prison, but he was able to plead benefit of clergy and after a short time was released.

Matters with Giles Alleyn were now coming to a head. The lease of the Theatre ground had long expired and nothing was settled. For the last few months the Company had left the Theatre and were playing in the Curtain. It was now clear that Alleyn meant to take advantage of a clause in the original lease, and unless something drastic was done the Burbages would lose their valuable property.

The chief sharers in the Company, Richard Burbage and his brother Cuthbert, Shakespeare, John Hemings, Augustine Phillips, Thomas Pope and Will Kemp, agreed to finance a new playhouse. In this new arrangement the Burbages held two and a half shares and the others one apiece. In addition, as playing members of the Company, each held an actor's share of the takings. A new site was found on the Bankside not far from the Rose Theatre, and the lease was signed on 25th December, 1598.

Three days later the two Burbages and a number of their friends, all armed, together with Peter Street, a builder who was to build the new playhouse, appeared outside the Theatre and proceeded to tear it down. As the Theatre was a timber building this did not take long. Giles Alleyn himself was away from London, but his people dared not interfere. The timber was then carried across the Thames and dumped on the new site. Meanwhile, until the new House was ready, the Company were still playing at the Curtain, where, early in April 1599, *Henry V* was produced.

The new playhouse—now the finest in London—was ready about July : it was called the Globe. By this time the Chamberlain's Men had a fine repertory, and their latest plays included the two parts of *Henry IV* and *Henry V* and Jonson's *Every Man in his Humour*. To these were soon added Jonson's *Every Man out of his Humour*, Shakespeare's *As You Like It*, and *Julius Caesar*.

The competition with the Admiral's Men now became acute. Even while the Chamberlain's Men were separated by the river and the City, there had been some feeling, but now that the two Companies were playing side by side the Admiral's Men soon felt the effects. Accordingly, in October, they set their dramatists to work to provide a counter-attraction. This was a new and more or less true version of the story of Sir John Oldcastle.

The play was put on for the first time on 1st November, and Henslowe, to show his appreciation, awarded the players ten shillings as a gift. It was, however, soon obvious that the competition of the Chamberlain's Men would be too much for the Admiral's, and Alleyn decided to build a new theatre north of the river in the parish of St. Giles. There were many vexatious delays, but ultimately, late in 1600, the new playhouse called the Fortune was finished and opened.

In the autumn of 1599 both Admiral's and Chamberlain's Men began to suffer from a new rival. William Stanley, Earl of Derby, was an enthusiastic amateur of plays. In November, at considerable cost, he revived the Company of the Children of Paul's. The children of the choir of St. Paul's Cathedral had not attempted to produce plays for the last nine years, but now the Earl of Derby set them going again, and John Marston, a young barrister who had recently distinguished himself as a virulent satirist, was brought in to provide them with plays. The investment was a success. As James Burbage had foreseen three years before, there was a great opening for small private playhouses which would cater solely for gentlemen.

Others were interested by the new playhouse. Henry Evans, who had been Lyly's partner in the former Boys' Company, saw a chance of starting another company of Boys. He went into partnership with the Master of the Chapel Royal, Nathaniel Giles. Giles, by authority of his office, was empowered to impress likely boys into the Royal choir. Evans had his eye on the empty Blackfriars Theatre, which was a considerable burden to the Burbages, for they had to find the rent but could make no use of it. The objections to the presence of professional players in the Blackfriars neighbourhood did not apply so strongly to semi-private performances by choir boys. Evans therefore hired the Blackfriars Playhouse from the Burbages on 2nd September, 1600, and in a very short time he had established another Children's Company, which was immediately prosperous.

Soon Ben Jonson, who seldom stayed long with one company, joined the Children of Blackfriars to provide plays for them. Marston offended Jonson by producing in his play *Histriomastix* a character called Chrysoganus, which was an obvious, though flattering, imitation of Jonson's Macilente in *Every Man out of his Humour*. Jonson was offended. He attacked Marston in his next play by making unpleasant hits at his person and his style. Marston countered, and for the next year a regular war of the Theatres was waged between the two Boy Companies.

Early in 1601 the Chamberlain's Men were again in trouble. The fortunes of the Earl of Essex were now at their lowest ; and he and his followers were planning a revolution. As part of their propaganda some of Essex's friends approached the Company and asked them to act *Richard II*. The players were not enthusiastic. The play had not been acted for some time and they did not believe that it would prove a good draw, but when Essex's friends promised to augment the takings with 40s. they agreed. Accordingly *Richard II* was acted on 7th February, 1601. The next day was Essex's futile rising. When the

Privy Council began to make enquiries the players were closely questioned about this affair, which was regarded as very sinister, but no action was taken and their indiscretion was overlooked.

Meanwhile the bickerings of the Children of Paul's and the Blackfriars were exciting genteel audiences. Both the professional Companies—Admiral's and Chamberlain's—felt the loss of their best customers. At last Ben Jonson, who was tiring of the struggle, decided to produce a play which would finally extinguish Marston. It was called *Poetaster*, and came out in the autumn of 1601. It was put on by the Children of Blackfriars.

The Chamberlain's Men and the Paul's Boys united to retaliate. They hired Thomas Dekker, who had hitherto written for the Admiral's, to compose an answer to Ben Jonson. His play was called *Satiromastix* and followed *Poetaster* very shortly. Dekker was so much more skilful at abuse that Ben Jonson retired from play-writing for a couple of years. Shakespeare himself seems to have taken some part in this controversy. In the Christmas holidays the undergraduates of St. John's College, Cambridge, acted a College play called *The Return from Parnassus*. They brought Burbage and Kemp in as actors to give a lesson in acting, and they made Kemp say, " That Ben Jonson's a pestilent fellow ; he brought up Horace giving the poet a pill, but our fellow Shakespeare has given him a purge that made him bewray his greed." This play or scene has apparently disappeared.

During these months Shakespeare wrote Hamlet, which was full of references to the events of the time.[1] About the same time he also wrote Twelfth Night, which was performed in the Hall of the Middle Temple on 2nd February, 1602.

In March 1603 Queen Elizabeth fell ill. As there was considerable doubt about the succession in the minds of the people at large, there was great alarm. On 19th March the Privy Council, who of late years had become increasingly suspicious of the Theatres, ordered all playing to cease. Five days later, Queen Elizabeth died.

The death of the Queen actually advanced the fortunes of the players, and especially of the Chamberlain's Men. One of the first acts of the new King was to take the Company under his own protection. On 19th May they became the King's Men, and a licence (see p. 40) was granted to them. There was, however, little playing that summer, for once again the plague broke out in the City of London and continued for nearly a year. The players, as usual, were obliged to go on tour, but at Christmas time they received a summons to come down to Wilton near Salisbury and there to play before the King and his Court. For this they received £30, for their expenses and for acting one

---

[1] For details see Hamlet in the "Penguin" Shakespeare.

play. By Christmas the plague was abating and the Court was held at Hampton Court. The Company acted six times in the Christmas holidays before the Court.

About this time Shakespeare wrote *Measure for Measure* and *All's Well That Ends Well*. In the autumn and winter of 1604–5 the players were much in request. On the 1st November they played *Othello* in the Banqueting House at Whitehall. On the 4th, *The Merry Wives of Windsor*. On the 26th December the *Comedy of Errors*; early in January *Love's Labour's Lost* and *Henry V*. On the 10th February they played *The Merchant of Venice*, which so pleased King James that he ordered it to be played again on the 12th.

Shakespeare was now apparently writing less for the Company, but in 1606 and again in 1607 he wrote at least two plays. *Lear* and *Macbeth* were probably written in 1606, and *Antony and Cleopatra* and *Coriolanus* probably in 1607.

There were many changes and developments during these years. The Boys' Companies flourished for some years and attracted to themselves some of the best writers of the time. Chapman was writing regularly for them, and in 1607 began the famous partnership of Francis Beaumont and John Fletcher, who wrote *Philaster* and *The Maid's Tragedy* for the Blackfriars Children.

In 1608, however, the Children of Blackfriars came

to an abrupt end. From the first they had been a nuisance to the authorities. The temptation to appeal to their small audiences by constantly commenting on current affairs was too great. In 1605 they had produced *Eastward Ho!*, a play written by Jonson, Marston and Chapman, in which they even had the impudence to mimic King James's Scots accent; it caused considerable trouble. In 1608 they offended unforgivably. Chapman wrote a play called *The Conspiracy and Tragedy of Charles, Duke of Byron*, which dealt with the rebellion and death of the Duke in Paris. It was recent history, and concerned living persons. Chapman even brought on the stage the reigning French King, Henri IV, together with his Queen and his mistress. In one scene the Queen was shown boxing the ears of her rival. The French Ambassador protested, and the Boys were forbidden to act the play. Soon afterwards, when the Court had left London, they disobeyed this order. As a result the Company was dissolved. Evans and his partners in the Blackfriars were now left with an empty playhouse on their hands, and they asked the Burbages to release them from their agreement.

The King's Men welcomed the chance. Conditions had changed considerably in the last eleven years, and there was no longer any serious opposition to the players occupying the Blackfriars playhouse. Moreover, the Globe Theatre was found to have its drawbacks. It was built on marshy ground, which in winter became very muddy. Accordingly, in August 1608, Richard Burbage took into partnership his brother Cuthbert, Shakespeare, Hemings, Condell and Sly, and his former tenant Evans. They took over the private playhouse for winter use, and, in addition, they purchased the plays belonging to the Children and agreed to employ their dramatists.

The different conditions in the private playhouses are reflected in the plays produced after the death of Queen Elizabeth. The Globe Theatre was open to the air and plays were acted by daylight. In the Blackfriars Theatre plays were acted by candlelight. Far more elaborate stage effects were therefore possible. Moreover, as the players now mainly concerned themselves with a better-class audience, drama tended to become more sophisticated and less public.

Shakespeare appears to have written little between 1608 and 1610. Then in 1610 and 1611 he wrote the three last plays, Cymbeline, the Winter's Tale, and The Tempest. The Tempest was acted for the King on 1st November, 1611, and the Winter's Tale on 5th November. Shakespeare, however, seems now to have spent most of his time at Stratford. On the 2nd July, 1613, his career as a dramatist was symbolically ended by the destruction of the Globe Theatre. The Players were acting Henry VIII with considerable magnificence. The disaster caused much comment, and there are a number of references to it. The

most detailed is in a letter written by Sir Henry
Wotton :

> " Now, to let matters of State sleep, I will entertain you at the
> present with what hath happened this week at the Bankside.   The
> King's Players had a new play, called *All is True,* representing some
> principal pieces of the reign of *Henry VIII,* which was set forth with
> many extraordinary circumstances of pomp and majesty, even to the
> matting of the stage ; the Knights of the Order, with their Georges
> and Garter, the guards with their embroidered coats, and the like :
> sufficient in truth within a while to make greatness very familiar, if
> not ridiculous.   Now, King *Henry* making a masque at the Cardinal
> Wolsey's house, and certain cannons being shot off at his entry,
> some of the paper, or other stuff, wherewith one of them was stopped,
> did light on the thatch, where being thought at first but an idle
> smoke, and their eyes more attentive to the show, it kindled inwardly,
> and ran round like a train, consuming within less than an hour the
> whole house to the very ground.
> " This was the fatal period of that virtuous Fabrique ; wherein yet
> nothing did perish, but wood and straw, and a few forsaken cloaks ;
> only one man had his breeches set on fire, that would perhaps have
> broiled him, if he had not by the benefit of a provident wit put it out
> with Bottle-Ale."

It is possible that the disaster was greater than
Wotton realised, for it may be that a number of
Shakespeare's plays perished in the fire.

CHAPTER V

THE ELIZABETHAN PLAYHOUSE

DRAMA, of all forms of art, is most immediately affected by material circumstance. The poet or the novelist can wait for recognition, perhaps for years, but a dramatist, and especially one who is also a sharer in the playhouse and company which produces his plays, cannot afford a failure. He must please his public or he will go bankrupt. He appeals, not to future ages, but to the audience of the afternoon. His plays therefore must be written to suit the stage on which they will be performed, the company which is to act them, and the audience which will pay to see them.

Until James Burbage built the Theatre in 1576 Elizabethan players had no permanent home. They were accustomed to act on a variety of stages. They gave private performances in the great halls of noblemen's houses or one of the Queen's palaces, or the Inns of Court, and they acted in public in Town Halls and inn yards, or in any place where they could erect a stage and collect a crowd.

Little is known for certain of the design of Burbage's Theatre, or indeed of the exact details of the other playhouses, but the general features can be

deduced from the many stage directions in the
original Quartos, or the First Folio of Shakespeare's

THE SWAN THEATRE: A SKETCH MADE IN 1596

plays, to go no farther. The existence, for instance,
of two doors and an upper stage is shown by such
directions as Enter one Citizen at one door, and another

at the other, and *Enter Richard aloft, between two Bishops.*[1]

Only one contemporary sketch of the stage exists. It is of the Swan, and was made from memory by a

THE COURTYARD OF THE NEW INN AT GLOUCESTER

Dutch traveller named De Witt in 1596 ; but his memory seems to have been as slight as his drawing.

James Burbage's Theatre apparently combined the features of the inn yard and the great hall. Inns in the 16th century were built round a courtyard, and the guests' rooms opened on to galleries which

[1] *Richard III*, II. iii and III. iv.

looked down into this yard. The stage was erected at one end, on barrel heads or trestles, and spectators from the street stood in the yard, whilst the more respectable spectators sat in the galleries. The best surviving specimen of a medieval inn, where also plays are known to have been acted, is The New Inn at Gloucester.

There are many examples of the great hall : in the colleges at Oxford and Cambridge, the Halls of the Inns of Court in London, Hampton Court and elsewhere. They are all of a pattern. At one end is the dais where the more illustrious sit ; at the other the " screens " through which are two doors leading to the kitchens beneath the " minstrels' gallery." With this screen as background, the players acted, using both doors and gallery as part of their stage. (See illustration facing page 97.)

In the playhouse the seating arrangements of inns and the form of the stage of the great hall were combined.

The Theatre, as has been seen, was built in 1576, and the Globe in 1599. When Henslowe and Alleyn decided to build the Fortune in 1600 they employed the builder of the Globe, and drew up a detailed and elaborate agreement. It is so important a document of stage history that it is worth reproducing in full :

" THIS INDENTURE made the eighth day of January, 1599 [1600], and in the two and fortieth year of the reign of our sovereign Lady Elizabeth, by the grace of God Queen of England, France and

THE ELIZABETHAN PLAYHOUSE

Ireland, defender of the faith, &c., Between Phillip Henslowe and
Edward Alleyn of the parish of Saint Saviours in Southwark, in the
county of Surrey, gentlemen, on the one part, And Peter Street,
citizen and carpenter of London, on the other part, WITNESSETH
that, whereas the said Phillip Henslowe and Edward Alleyn the day
of the date hereof have bargained, compounded and agreed with the
said Peter Street for the erecting, building, and setting up of a new
house and stage for a playhouse, in and upon a certain plot or parcel
of ground appointed out for that purpose, situate and being near
Golding Lane in the parish of Saint Giles without Cripplegate of
London To be by him the said Peter Street, or some other sufficient
workmen of his providing and appointment, and at his proper costs
and charges, for the consideration hereafter in these presents
expressed, made, erected, builded and set up, in manner and form
following ; that is to say,

" The frame of the said house to be set square, and to contain
fourscore foot of lawful assize every way square without, and fifty-
five foot of like assize square every way within, with a good, sure, and
strong foundation of piles, brick, lime, and sand, both without and
within, to be wrought one foot of assize at the least above the ground.

" And the said frame to contain three stories in height, The first
or lower story to contain twelve foot of lawful assize in height,
The second story eleven foot of lawful assize in height, And the
third or upper story to contain nine foot of lawful assize in height.

" All which stories shall contain twelve foot and a half of lawful
assize in breadth throughout, besides a jutty forwards in either of the
said two upper stories of ten inches of lawful assize, with four
convenient divisions for gentlemen's rooms, and other sufficient and
convenient divisions for twopenny rooms, with necessary seats to
be placed and set as well in those rooms as throughout all the rest
of the galleries of the said house ; and with such like stairs, conveyances, and divisions, without and within, as are made and contrived
in and to the late erected playhouse on the Bank, in the said parish
of Saint Saviours, called the Globe ;

" With a Stage and Tiring-house to be made, erected and set up
within the said frame, with a shadow or cover over the said stage,
which stage shall be placed and set, as also the staircases of the
said frame, in such sort as is prefigured in a plot thereof drawn,

" And which stage shall contain in length forty and three foot of
lawful assize, and in breadth to extend to the middle of the yard of
the said house,

" The same stage to be paled in below with good strong and sufficient new oaken boards,

" And likewise the lower story of the said frame withinside, and the same lower story to be also laid over and fenced with strong iron pikes,

" And the said stage to be in all other proportions contrived and fashioned like unto the stage of the said playhouse called the Globe ; with convenient windows and lights glazed to the said tiring-house,

" And the said frame, stage and staircases to be covered with tile, and to have a sufficient gutter of lead, to carry and convey the water from the covering of the said stage to fall backwards,

" And also all the said frame and the staircases thereof to be sufficiently enclosed without with lath, lime and hair, and the gentlemen's rooms and twopenny rooms to be sealed with lath, lime and hair ; and all the floors of the said galleries, stories and stage to be boarded with good and sufficient new deal boards of the whole thickness, where need shall be.

" And the said house, and other things before mentioned to be made and done, to be in all other contrivitions, conveyances, fashions, thing and things, effected, finished, and done according to the manner and fashion of the said house called the Globe,

" Saving only that all the principal and main posts of the said frame and stage forward, shall be square and wrought pilasterwise, with carved proportions called Satyrs to be placed and set on the top of every of the same posts.

" And saving also that the said Peter Street shall not be charged with any manner of painting in or about the said frame, house, or stage, or any part thereof, nor rendering the walls within nor ceiling any more or other rooms than the gentlemen's rooms, twopenny rooms and stage, before remembered.

" Now THEREUPON the said Peter Street doth covenant, promise and grant for himself, his executors and administrators, to and with the said Phillip Henslowe and Edward Alleyn, and either of them and the executors and administrators of them, and either of them by these presents, in manner and form following, that is to say,

" That he the said Peter Street, his executors or assigns, shall and will, at his or their own proper costs and charges, well, workmanlike and substantially make, erect, set up and fully finish in and by all things, according to the true meaning of these presents, with good, strong, and substantial new timber and other necessary stuff,

" All the said frame and other works whatsoever in and upon the

THE HALL OF THE MIDDLE TEMPLE

(*From the dais*)

said plot or parcel of ground (being not by any authority restrained, and having ingress, egress and regress to do the same) before the five and twentieth day of July next coming after the date hereof ;

" AND SHALL ALSO at his or their like costs and charges, provide and find all manner of workmen, timber, joists, rafters, boards, doors, bolts, hinges, brick, tile, lath, lime, hair, sand, nails, lead, iron, glass, workmanship and other things whatsoever, which shall be needful, convenient and necessary for the said frame and works and every part thereof,

" And shall also make all the said frame in every point for scantlings larger and bigger in assize than the scantlings of the timber of the said new erected house called the Globe.

" AND ALSO that he the said Peter Street shall forthwith, as well by himself as by such other and so many workmen as shall be convenient and necessary, enter into and upon the said buildings and works,

" And shall in reasonable manner proceed therein, without any wilful detraction until the same shall be fully effected and finished.

" IN CONSIDERATION of all which buildings, and of all stuff and workmanship hereto belonging,

" The said Phillip Henslowe and Edward Alleyn, and either of them, for themselves, their and either of their executors and administrators, do jointly and severally covenant to grant to and with the said Peter Street, his executors and administrators, by these presents,

" That they, the said Phillip Henslowe and Edward Alleyn, or one of them or the executors, administrators or assigns of them or one of them, shall and will well and truly pay or cause to be paid unto the said Peter Street, his executors or assigns, at the place aforesaid appointed for the erecting of the said frame, The full sum of four hundred and forty pounds of lawful money of England, in manner and form following, that is to say, At such time And when as the timber work of the said frame shall be raised and set up by the said Peter Street, his executors or assigns, or within seven days then next following, two hundred and twenty pounds,

" And at such time and when as the said frame and work shall be fully effected and finished as is aforesaid, or within seven days then next following, the other two hundred and twenty pounds, without fraud or covin.

" PROVIDED ALWAYS, and it is agreed between the said parties, That whatsoever sum or sums of money the said Phillip Henslowe and Edward Alleyn, or either of them, or the executors or assigns of them or either of them shall lend or deliver unto the said Peter Street, his executors or assigns or any other by his appointment or consent, for or concerning the said works or any part thereof, or any stuff thereto belonging, before the raising and setting up of the said frame, shall be reputed, accepted, taken and accounted in part of the first payment aforesaid of the said sum of four hundred and forty pounds ;

" And all such sum and sums of money as they, or any of them, shall as aforesaid lend or deliver between the raising of the said frame and finishing thereof, and of all the rest of the said works, shall be reputed, accepted, taken and accounted in part of the last payment aforesaid of the same sum of four hundred and forty pounds ; any thing abovesaid to the contrary not withstanding.

" IN WITNESS WHEREOF the parties abovesaid to these present indentures interchangeably have set their hands and seals. Given the day and year first above-written." [1]

It is not always remembered that the Elizabethan playhouse was very small. The external dimensions of the theatre measured 80 by 80 feet ; and of the interior area of 55 feet by 55, the stage occupied almost half. Henslowe's Fortune was square, but the pictures which remain of the outside of other theatres show that they were circular or hexagonal. Within there were three tiers of galleries looking down upon the yard or pit where the poorer spectators stood, or possibly sat on stools. The stage itself, which is technically called an " apron stage," jutted out into the yard, so that when the house was crowded the players were surrounded on three sides. Over the stage there was a " shadow " or roof which protected the players from the rain. At the back

---

[1] *Henslowe Papers*, edited by W. W. Greg, p. 4.

of the stage on either side there were two entrances
by side doors. By these the characters entered and
disappeared. It was a convenient arrangement,
leading to some easy symbolism. When two nations

THE EXTERIOR OF THE GLOBE PLAYHOUSE,
FROM VISSCHER'S VIEW OF LONDON, 1616.

were at war, one side is England and the other
France. When a procession passes over the stage,
it enters at one door and goes out by the other.

Over the back of the stage there ran a gallery or
upper stage, which could be used whenever any

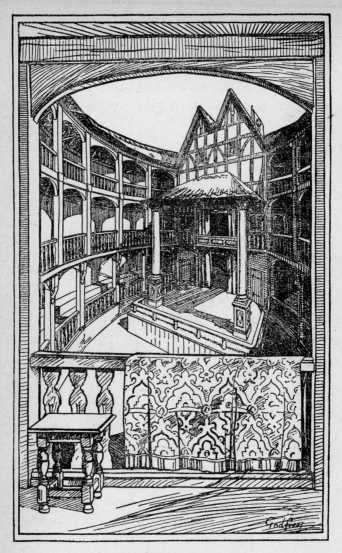

AN ELIZABETHAN PLAYHOUSE.

A reconstruction by Walter H. Godfrey.

100

upper scene was needed. It was the walls of Berkeley Castle whence King Richard the Second addressed Bolingbroke below. It was Cleopatra's monument whither the dying Antony was hoisted up. In *King John* it served for the walls of Angers whence citizens addressed the king, and later the prison walls from which little Arthur leaps down. Probably in *Lear* it stood for Dover Cliff whence blinded Gloucester tries to commit suicide. Occasionally it was used for heaven. The balcony also enabled plays to be acted at different levels.

The space at the back of the stage underneath the balcony was known as the " tiring-house " or " the place behind the stage." Usually it was curtained off, but when the curtains were drawn it provided a convenient inner stage for a variety of purposes— tombs, caves, studies, bedrooms. The inner stage was much used, especially for set scenes such as taverns, or bedrooms. There was no general curtain concealing the whole stage, so that all scenes on the main stage began with an entrance and ended with an exit. In tragedies, unless the dead died within the curtains, a funeral procession gave a fitting close.

The stage directions of the early editions of plays are usually scant and formal, but at times they will indicate the production.

There are two early Quartos of *Romeo & Juliet*, and both contain illuminating stage directions which show how the play was produced. In Act I, Scene iv, Benvolio, Mercutio and Romeo are on their way to the feast at Capulet's house. After some talk *They march about the stage, and serving men come forth with napkins.* The walk indicates that they are going, and the serving men that they have arrived at the feast. The serving men speak to each other, and then *Enter all the guests and gentlewomen to the Maskers.* Capulet welcomes them : *Music plays and they dance.*

The directions in Act III, Scene v, show how the balcony was used. Romeo has spent the night with Juliet. The scene begins with *Enter Romeo and Juliet at the window.* Romeo gives her a farewell kiss. *He goeth down.* When he has made his exit, Juliet addresses fickle Fortune, then *She goeth down from the window : Enter Lady Capulet*—on the stage below, where the rest of the scene follows. Thus at the beginning of the scene the audience see the outside of Juliet's bedroom, but when Lady Capulet enters the scene is supposed to change to the interior. A literal-minded reader may be disturbed at this simplicity, but on the Elizabethan stage it was no more distracting than the abrupt cuts in a film to an experienced cinema-goer.

The scene where Juliet is discovered apparently dead shows the use of the curtains and the inner stage. Capulet has decreed that Juliet shall be married in the morning. *Exeunt Juliet and Nurse,*—

through the curtains at the back of the stage. After Capulet and Lady Capulet have talked together, *Enter Juliet and Nurse* : the curtains are drawn aside, showing the bed which had already been set up in the inner stage. Juliet is left alone and drinks the friar's sleeping draught. *She falls upon her bed within the curtains*, which are then closed. The action continues on the front stage. *Enter Lady Capulet and Nurse with herbs* . . . *Enter Capulet* . . . *Exeunt Lady Capulet and Nurse* . . . *Enter three or four with spits, and logs, and baskets* . . . *Music* . . . *Enter Nurse* . . . Capulet speaks to the Nurse :

> " Go waken Juliet, go and trim her up,
>   I'll go and chat with Paris, hie, make haste,
>   Make haste, the bridegroom, he is come already,
>   Make haste I say."
>
> > [*Exit.*

There is no exit marked for the Nurse. She goes to the back of the stage and draws the curtains, revealing Juliet lying on the bed. She discovers Juliet apparently dead and calls out for help. *Enter Lady Capulet* . . . *Enter Capulet* . . . *Enter Friar and the County* . . . Having lamented Juliet's death, *They all but the Nurse go forth, casting rosemary on her and shutting the curtains.* The action then continues on the main stage until the end.

In the last scene the stage directions are——*Enter County Paris and his page with flowers and sweet water*

. . . *Paris strews the tomb with flowers* . . . *The Page whistles and calls :* My Lord . . . *Enter Romeo and his man Balthasar with a torch, mattock, and a crow of iron* . . . *Romeo opens the tomb*—that is, he draws aside the curtains, revealing Juliet lying on a bier. Paris comes forward and encounters him. They fight . . . *Exit the Page* . . . *Paris Dies* . . . Romeo then draws attention to Juliet, and " fixes the locality " :

> " For here lies Juliet, and her beauty makes
> This vault a feasting presence full of light."

He takes the poison and *Falls* . . . *Enter Friar with a lantern, crow, and spade* . . . *Friar stoops and looks on the blood and weapons* . . . *Juliet rises* . . . *Exit Friar Laurence* . . . *Enter Boy and Watch* . . . Juliet hears them approaching. *She stabs herself and falls— by the bier over Romeo's body. Enter Romeo's man* . . . *Enter Friar and another Watchman* . . . *Enter the Prince* . . . *Enter Capulet and his Wife* . . . *Enter Montague* . . . The sorrowing parents behold the tragedy of the lovers. Then the Prince says—

> " Seal up the mouth of outrage for a while."

At these words the curtains are drawn together, and the story is brought effectively to its close, with the two fathers reconciled before the curtain which now conceals the bodies of the dead lovers.

The structure of the stage considerably affected plays. On the apron stage the actor came forward right into the midst of his audience, and was therefore in the closest possible touch. He was not, as in the modern theatre, divided from them by a curtain or by light and darkness. Hence the device of soliloquy was perfectly natural. The actor explains his position and his thoughts to those who are immediately in front of him. Moreover he was so close that there was no need for him to shout, so that the greatest subtlety of voice, gesture and expression was possible.

There was apparently no scenery, and plays were acted in daylight. The Elizabethan actor was thus without the effects produced on the modern stage by lighting, scenery—realistic or symbolic—and elaborate orchestral effects. In their place he gained his effects by a direct assault on the emotions and the imagination of the spectators. Poetry was a natural medium for dramatic speech, especially at exalted moments, and a good actor could carry his audience with him by the emotional effect of rhetoric.

A scene ended when all the actors had gone off the stage and a new set of characters came on. There was thus a quick continuity of performance with no break in the illusion. As there was no scenery, so there was no limit to the number of scenes. Usually the exact locality of the scene was unimportant.

When it was necessary, Shakespeare showed it in the dialogue.

"What country, friends, is this?" Viola asks.

"This is Illyria, lady," the sea captain answers.

But for the most part a simple property or garment was sufficient. Chairs or stools showed indoor scenes ; a man wearing riding-boots was a messenger ; a king wearing his armour was on the field of battle ; a watchman carrying a lantern indicated the streets of a city at night. The most important difference between the modern and the Elizabethan theatre is that Elizabethan plays were all acted by daylight.

Such arrangements are simple, but not crude. All drama implies an acceptance of conventions and a use of the imagination, and properties can easily replace scenery. The properties were many and varied. Amongst the Henslowe *Papers* is a complete inventory of the properties belonging to the Admiral's Company in 1598 :

i rock, i cage, i tomb, i Hell mouth.
i tomb of Guido, i tomb of Dido, i bedstead.
viii lances, i pair of stairs for Phaeton.
ii steeples, & i chime of bells, & i beacon.
i heifer for the play of Phaeton, the limbs dead.
i globe, & i golden sceptre ; iii clubs.
ii marchpanes, & the City of Rome.
i golden fleece ; ii rackets ; i bay tree.
i wooden hatchet ; i leather hatchet.
i wooden canopy ; old Mahomet's head.
i lion skin ; i bear's skin ; & Phaeton's limbs & Phaeton's chariot ;
    & Argus' head.
Neptune's fork and garland.

i " crosers " staff ; Kent's wooden leg.

Iris head, & rainbow ; i little altar.

viii visards ; Tamberlain's bridle ; i wooden mattock.

Cupid's bow, & quiver ; the cloth of the Sun & Moon.

i boar's head & Cerberus' iii heads.

i Caduceus ; ii moss banks, & i snake.

ii fanes of feathers ; Bellendon stable ; i tree of golden apples ;
    Tantalus' tree, ix iron targets.

i copper target, & xvii foils.

iiii wooden targets ; i greeve armour.

i sign for Mother Redcap ; i buckler.

Mercury's wings ; Tasso's picture ; i helmet with a dragon ;
    i shield, with iii lions ; i elm bowl.

i chain of dragons ; i gilt spear.

ii coffins ; i bull's head ; and i " vylter."

iii timbrels ; i dragon in Faustus.

i lion ; ii lion heads ; i great horse with his legs ; i sackbut.

i wheel and frame in the Siege of London.

i pair of wrought gloves.

i Pope's mitre.

iii Imperial crowns ; i plain crown.

i ghost's crown ; i crown with a sun.

i frame for the heading in Black Joan.

i black dog.

i cauldron for the Jew.[1]

[This list is reproduced in modern spelling. Henslowe's spelling was erratic and individual, and some of the interpretations are questionable. It is not known how " Hell mouth " or the " City of Rome " were represented as properties. Of the others, a " marchpane " was an elaborate marzipan cake ; the " frame for the heading " was a piece of stage machinery to produce the illusion of a be-heading.]

There was some attempt at realistic presentation. When characters were stabbed they bled, as Caesar is made to bleed in *Julius Caesar*. In the play of

[1] *Henslowe Papers*, p. 116.

Arden of Feversham there was a fog, which must have been represented somehow. The stage machinery was, however, crude and irritating to the artistic sense of Ben Jonson, who sneered at it in the prologue to *Every Man in his Humour* :

> " He rather prays you will be pleased to see
> One such to-day, as other plays should be ;
> Where neither chorus wafts you o'er the seas,
> Nor creaking throne comes down the boys to please ;
> Nor nimble squib is seen to make afeard
> The gentlewomen ; nor rolled bullet heard
> To say, it thunders ; nor tempestuous drum
> Rumbles, to tell you when the storm doth come."

On the other hand costumes were sometimes lavish and imposing. When the Admiral's Men produced a play of Cardinal Wolsey in 1601 they bought " two pile velvet of carnadine at twenty shillings a yard, satins at twelve shillings and taffetas at twelve and six." The bill for material alone came to £21.

There was an elaborate system of trumpet calls ; sennets, tuckets, alarums, retreats, flourishes, appear frequently in stage directions. No king enters or goes out without a flourish. On the modern stage these trumpet calls are usually half-hearted ; on the Elizabethan they had a considerable psychological effect. The stage directions, especially of some plays produced at the Rose Theatre, show that the stage carpenter was ambitious.

" *Let there be a brazen head set in the middle of the place behind the Stage,*
  out of which cast flames of fire, drums rumble within : Enter two
  Priests."

" *Exit Venus ; or if you conveniently can, let a chair come down from the*
  top of the stage and draw her up."

" *The Magi with their rods beat the ground, and from under the same riseth*
  a brave arbour ; the King returneth in another suit, while the
  Trumpets sound."

" *Upon this prayer she departeth, and a flame of fire appeareth from beneath,*
  and Radagon is swallowed."

" *Jonas the Prophet cast out of the Whale's belly upon the stage.*"

Plays at the Rose Theatre were acted on the
repertory system. The Company kept a considerable range of plays available and played a different
play each afternoon. The average life of a new play
was about ten performances. Popular plays were
acted more often, but the less successful sometimes
disappeared after the second or third performance.
Continuous runs were unknown. Thus a typical
fortnight—1st–14th February, 1596—shows that the
Admiral's Men played the following plays :

> *The Jew of Malta.*
> *1st part of Fortunatus.*
> *The Wise Men of Westchester.*
> *Longshanks.*
> *Harry the Fifth.*
> *Crack me these Nuts.*
> *Pythagoras.*
> *Fortunatus.*
> *Chinon of England.*
> *The Blind Beggar of Alexandria.*
> *Dr. Faustus.*
> *Pythagoras.*

Thus on twelve acting days ten different plays were acted. Of these one—*The Blind Beggar of Alexandria*—was a new play, and six no longer survive. A large proportion of Elizabethan plays have perished.

It follows that the Elizabethan actor was a busy man, constantly rehearsing new plays. He had little time for long, elaborate and exhausting preparations ; but he belonged to a team and the trained actor was ready in emergency to improvise, and indeed Italian actors at this time were so clever that, given a story, they could make up the play as they went along.

The Elizabethan acting company was a " fellowship of players," and they worked on the share system. The actors were partners in the concern, and therefore the company remained constant. There were ten to fifteen regular sharers, and in addition some hired men and boys learning the business who ultimately might rise to be sharers.

Amongst Henslowe's papers there is an agreement between Henslowe and Jacob Meade with an actor named Robert Dawes. Dawes agrees for a space of three years to play with such company as Phillip Henslowe and Jacob Meade shall agree ; " at the rate of one whole share according to the custom of the players ; and that he the said Robert Dawes shall and will at all times during the said term duly attend all such rehearsal which shall the night before the rehearsal be given publicly out ; and if that he the said Robert Dawes shall at any time fail to come at the hour appointed, then he shall and will pay to the said Phillip Henslowe and Jacob Meade their executors or assigns twelve pence ; and that if he come not before the said rehearsal is ended then the said Robert Dawes is contented to pay two shillings ; and further that if the said Robert Dawes shall not every day whereon any play is or ought to be played be ready apparelled and . . . to begin the play at the hour of three of the clock in the afternoon unless by six of the same company he shall be licensed to the contrary, that then he the said Robert Dawes shall and will pay unto the said Phillip and Jacob or their assigns three shillings, and that if he the said Robert Dawes happen to be overcome with drink at the time when he ought to play, by the judgment of four of the said company, he shall and will pay ten shillings and if he the said Robert Dawes shall fail to come during any play having no license or just excuse of sickness he is contented to pay twenty shillings."

The agreement then proceeds to discuss the problem of wearing-apparel and adds the clause that if Dawes " shall at any time after the play is ended depart or go out of the house with any of their apparel on his body or if the said Robert Dawes shall carry away any property belonging to the said company, or shall be consenting or privy to any other of the said company going out of the house with any of their apparel on his or their bodies, he the said Robert Dawes shall and will forfeit and pay unto the said Phillip and Jacob or their administrators or assigns the sum of forty pounds of lawful money of England."

The importance of the company system is considerable. Shakespeare had to write for his company as it existed. Nowadays a producer will assemble actors suitable for a particular play, and he can draw from a vast reservoir of all kinds and types. If he needs an actor who specialises in taking the part of a chimpanzee, he will find several available. Shakespeare had to write for his company as it existed. He could not therefore produce characters for which the company had no physical representative. On the other hand he made use of the peculiarities of the actors, and it is noticeable how certain physical types recur. In the company there was a tall man with a thin hatchet face ; another who specialised in " silly gentleman " parts. Richard Burbage, the chief tragedian, matures. There were no young Romeos as a chief character in Shakespeare's later plays. Instead his heroes are mature men : Othello, Lear, Prospero. The changes are not less noticeable in the girls' parts. No women actresses appeared in Shakespeare's time—nor indeed until the Restoration—and women's parts were taken by boys. The boy actor is not necessarily a disadvantage. As boys could only act women's parts until their voices broke, Shakespeare was spared Rosalinds and Violas of forty. There were not more than two or three boys at once, and therefore not many women in any one play.

CHAPTER VI

THE SHAKESPEARE CANON

In any study of the development of Shakespeare's art it is necessary first to discover the date when each play was written. This is not so easy. So few of the necessary records survive that it is seldom possible to date any Elizabethan play exactly. Plays acted by the companies which played in Henslowe's theatres are recorded in his diary, which gives either the date of the first performance, or else details of the payments made to dramatists. But only a small proportion of the plays written during Shakespeare's lifetime were acted at the Rose or Fortune Playhouses. For the other companies and playhouses there is no record comparable to the *Diary*.

Shakespeare's plays must therefore be dated by argument, and deduction from such evidence as can be collected. This is of three kinds : (*a*) external ; (*b*) internal ; (*c*) style. By combining all kinds of evidence the canon of the plays has been worked out, and there is general agreement on the approximate dates on which most of the plays were written.

The most valuable kind of evidence is external, that is, a clear mention or reference to a particular play. There are many of these references. Thus in *Gesta Grayorum*, an account of the famous " Gray's Inn Revels " of 1594–5, there is a note that :

" on the night of the 28th December, 1594, after dancing and revelling with gentlewomen, a ' Comedy of Errors ' (like to Plautus his ' Menechmus ') was played by the players."

A German traveller named Platter who visited London in 1599 noted in his diary that :

" After dinner on the 21st of September, at about two o'clock, I went with my companions over the water, and in the strewn roof-house saw the tragedy of the first Emperor Julius with at least fifteen characters very well acted. At the end of the comedy they danced according to their custom with extreme elegance. Two in men's clothes and two in women's gave this performance, in wonderful combination with each other." [1]

John Manningham, a Barrister of the Middle Temple, recorded in his diary under the date 2nd February, 1602 :

" At our feast we had a play called ' Twelfth Night, or What you Will,' much like the Comedy of Errors, or Menechmi in Plautus, but most like and near to that in Italian called *Inganni*. A Good practice in it to make the Steward believe his Lady widow was in love with him, by counterfeiting a letter as from his Lady in general terms, telling him what she liked best in him, and prescribing his gesture in smiling, his apparel, etc., and then when he came to practise making believe they took him to be mad."

The " Revels Accounts " of the Court show that payments were made in 1604–5 for a performance of

---

[1] E. K. Chambers : *The Elizabethan Stage*, ii, pp. 364–5.

Othello before King James I and his Court on 1st November, on 4th November *The Merry Wives of Windsor*, and the 26th December *Measure for Measure*. In January for *Love's Labour's Lost*, on 7th January for *Henry V*, on 10th February for *The Merchant of Venice*, which so pleased King James that he commanded a second performance on the 12th. Later, payments were made for *The Tempest*, acted before the King on 1st November, 1611, and again in February 1613, on the marriage festivities of the Princess Elizabeth.

Valuable evidence for the dates of the earlier plays is given in Francis Meres' list of a dozen quoted on p. 13. These plays at least were produced before Meres' book went to press in the summer of 1598. Moreover it is probable that other plays, more important, had not then been produced, otherwise Meres would hardly have failed to mention *Hamlet, Othello* and *Lear*.

Such evidence as this seldom gives the date of the first performance of any play, but it certainly shows that the play had been written before a certain date.

The second kind of evidence is internal, where in the play itself there is some unmistakable reference to an identifiable event. There are not many of these in Shakespeare's plays, for although he often reminded his audience of current events in some significant speech, he seldom makes a direct reference.

There is, however, a clear reference to the triumphant departure on 27th March, 1599, of the Earl

of Essex for Ireland in the *Chorus* before Act V of
Henry V :

> " But now behold,
> In the quick forge and working-house of thought,
> How London doth pour out her citizens,
> The Mayor and all his brethren in best sort,
> Like to the senators of th'antique Rome,
> With the plebeians swarming at their heels,
> Go forth and fetch their conquering Caesar in :
> As by a lower, but by loving likelihood,
> Were now the General of our gracious Empress,
> As in good time he may, from Ireland coming,
> Bringing rebellion broached on his sword ;
> How many would the peaceful City quit,
> To welcome him ? "

As Essex failed utterly and returned secretly to
London on 28th September, it follows that the
Chorus was written soon after March 1599.

In *Hamlet* there is a clear reference to the wars of
the theatres in 1600–1 in Hamlet's remarks :

HAMLET : What players are they ?

ROSENCRANTZ : Even those you were wont to take delight in, the
tragedians of the City.

HAMLET : How chances it they travel ? their residence both in
reputation and profit was better both ways.

ROSENCRANTZ : I think their inhibition comes by the means of the
late innovation.

HAMLET : Do they hold the same estimation they did when I was
in the City ? are they so follow'd ?

ROSENCRANTZ : No indeed, they are not.

HAMLET : How comes it ? do they grow rusty ?

ROSENCRANTZ : Nay, their endeavour keeps in the wonted pace ;
but there is sir an aery of children, little eyases, that cry out
on the top of question ; and are most tyrannically clapp'd for't :

these are now the fashion, and so berattle the common Stages (so they call them) that many wearing rapiers, are afraid of goose-quills, and dare scarce come thither.

HAMLET : What, are they children ? who maintains 'em ? how are they escoted ? Will they pursue the quality no longer than they can sing ? will they not say afterwards if they should grow themselves to common Players (as it is most like if their means are no better) their writers do them wrong, to make them exclaim against their own succession ?

ROSENCRANTZ : Faith there has been much to do on both sides : and the nation holds it no sin, to tarre them on to controversy. There was for a while, no money bid for argument, unless the Poet and the Player went to cuffs in the question.

HAMLET : Is't possible ?

GUILDENSTERN : O there has been much throwing about of brains.

HAMLET : Do the Boys carry it away ?

ROSENCRANTZ : Ay that they do my Lord, Hercules and his load too.

The third method of dating, by style, is not so exact. Nevertheless the changes and developments of Shakespeare's poetic style are so noticeable that a play can be reasonably placed by style alone in one of four groups—early, mature, concentrated and late. By a combination of the three methods the plays can be dated approximately, and roughly in the order of writing, so that it is possible not only to trace Shakespeare's development but also to see his plays against the background of his times.

Lear, for instance, was apparently written in 1606. It must have been written before the Christmas of that year, because on the 26th November, 1607, Nathaniel Butter and John Busby entered in the Stationers' Register :

" A book called Master William Shakespeare his history of King Lear, as it was played before the King's Majesty at Whitehall upon Saint Stephen's night at Christmas last, by his majesty's servants playing usually at the Globe on the Bankside."

The play was thus acted at the Court in the Christmas holidays of 1606. The earliest date for its writing was 1603. Edgar, disguised as " Poor Tom, the Bedlam beggar," mutters :

". . . five fiends have been in poor Tom at once ; of lust, as Obidicut, Hobbididance Prince of dumbness, Mahu of stealing, Modo of murder, Flibbertigibbet of mopping and mowing, who since possesses chambermaids and waiting women."

These names Shakespeare took from a book called A declaration of egregious popish impostures which was written by the Rev. Samuel Harsnett, Chaplain to the Bishop of London, and published early in 1603.

It is possible to get nearer. Gloucester in the play, who was a believer in omens and portents, says to Edgar :

" These late eclipses in the sun and moon portend no good to us : though the wisdom of Nature can reason it thus, and thus, yet Nature finds itself scourg'd by the sequent effects. Love cools, friendship falls off, brothers divide. In cities, mutinies ; in countries, discord ; in palaces, treason ; and the bond crack'd, 'twixt son and father. This villain of mine comes under the prediction ; there's son against father ; the King falls from bias of Nature, there's father against child. We have seen the best of our time. Machinations, hollowness, treachery, and all ruinous disorders follow us disquietly to our graves."

A little later Edmund cynically echoes him to Edgar :

"I am thinking, brother, of a prediction I read this other day, what should follow these eclipses. . . . I promise you, the effects he writes of, succeed unhappily, as of unnaturalness between the child and the parent, death, dearth, dissolutions of ancient amities, divisions in state, menaces and maledictions against King and nobles, needless diffidences, banishment of friends, dissipation of cohorts, nuptial breaches, and I know not what."

Shakespeare took these speeches from a little pamphlet called *Strange, fearful and true news which happened at Carlstadt in the Kingdom of Croatia.* It was translated from the High Dutch and told of terrible signs and portents which (according to the editor, one Edward Gresham, an almanack maker) were divine portents of threatening disaster :

"The Earth's and Moon's late and horrible obscurations, the frequent eclipsations of the fixed bodies ; by the wandering, the fixed stars, I mean the planets, within these few years more than ordinary, shall without doubt (salved divine inhibition) have their effects no less admirable, than the positions unusual. Which PEUCER with many more too long to rehearse out of continual observation and the consent of all authors noted to be, new leagues, traitorous designments, catching at kingdoms, translation of empire, downfall of men in authority, emulations, ambition, innovations, factious sects, schisms and much disturbance and troubles in religion and matters of the Church, with many other things infallible in sequent such orbical positions and phenomenes."

The preface to this work is dated 11th February, 1606. It follows that *Lear* was written between this date and its performance in the Christmas of the same year. The style, too, of the play, with its concentrated and pregnant imagery, shows that it was written about the same time as *Macbeth* and after *Hamlet* and *Othello*. There is some definite evidence for assigning *Macbeth* also to the same year, 1606.

The full list of Shakespeare's plays with their approximate dates is as follows :

	PLAYS		FIRST PRINTED
1591.	HENRY VI *three parts*	. . . . .	Folio 1623
	RICHARD III	. . . .	1597
	TITUS ANDRONICUS	. . . . . .	1594
	LOVE'S LABOUR'S LOST	. . . .	1598
	THE TWO GENTLEMEN OF VERONA	. .	Folio
	THE COMEDY OF ERRORS	. . .	Folio
	THE TAMING OF THE SHREW	. . .	Folio
1594.	ROMEO AND JULIET	(*pirated* 1597)	1599
	A MIDSUMMER NIGHT'S DREAM	. . .	1600
	RICHARD II	. . . . . .	1597
	KING JOHN	. . . . .	Folio
	THE MERCHANT OF VENICE	. .	1600
1597.	HENRY IV *part i*	. . . . .	1598
	HENRY IV *part ii*	. . . . .	1600
	MUCH ADO ABOUT NOTHING	. .	1600
	MERRY WIVES OF WINDSOR	(*pirated* 1602)	Folio
	AS YOU LIKE IT	. . .	Folio
	JULIUS CAESAR	. . . .	Folio
	HENRY V	. . .	(*pirated* 1600) Folio
	TROILUS AND CRESSIDA	. . .	1609
1601.	HAMLET	. . .	(*pirated* 1603) 1604
	TWELFTH NIGHT	. . . .	Folio
	MEASURE FOR MEASURE	. . .	Folio
	ALL'S WELL THAT ENDS WELL	. .	Folio
	OTHELLO	. . . . . .	1622
1606.	LEAR	. . . . . .	1608
	MACBETH	. . . . .	Folio
	TIMON OF ATHENS	. . .	Folio

	PLAYS				FIRST PRINTED
	ANTONY AND CLEOPATRA	.	.	.	. *Folio*
	CORIOLANUS .	.	.	.	. *Folio*
1609.	PERICLES .	.	.	(*omitted from the Folio*)	1609
1611.	CYMBELINE .	.	.	.	. *Folio*
	THE WINTER'S TALE	.	.	.	. *Folio*
	THE TEMPEST .	.	.	.	. *Folio*
	HENRY VIII (*with John Fletcher*)	.	.	.	. *Folio*

CHAPTER VII

DEVELOPMENT OF SHAKESPEARE'S STYLE

WHEN Shakespeare began to write for the stage the standard of acting was set by Edward Alleyn, and of plays by those who wrote for him, especially Marlowe, Greene and Kyd. Alleyn's most popular plays were Marlowe's *Tamburlaine* and *Jew of Malta*, Greene's *Orlando Furioso* and *Friar Bacon*, and Kyd's *Spanish Tragedy*. All had much in common, and at first Shakespeare imitated the common style and mannerisms so closely that some critics argue hotly whether he was indeed the sole author of some of the early plays attributed to him in the First Folio.

Audiences in the early 1590's were still unsophisticated, simple in their demands, and hearty in their appetites. They expected characters on the stage to talk in high-sounding phrases and to make long speeches on every occasion, full of rhetorical devices, stuffed with mythology and bookish similes. Thus Marlowe, wishing to express the perplexities of Zenocrate, torn between affection for her father and her former lover, and her new love for Tamburlaine, is made to say :

" Now shame and duty, love and fear presents
  A thousand sorrows to my martyred soul.
  Whom should I wish the fatal victory,
  When my poor pleasures are divided thus,
  And racked by duty from my cursed heart ?
  My father and my first betrothed love
  Must fight against my life and present love ;
  Wherein the change I use condemns my faith,
  And makes my deeds infamous through the world.
  But as the gods, to end the Trojan's toil,
  Prevented Turnus of Lavinia,
  And fatally enriched Aeneas' love,
  So, for a final issue to my griefs,
  To pacify my country and my love,
  Must Tamburlaine by their resistless powers,
  With virtue of a gentle victory,
  Conclude a league of honour to my hope ;
  Then, as the powers divine have pre-ordained,
  With happy safety of my father's life
  Send like defence of fair Arabia."

This is the language of the literary student who turns naturally to Virgil for an apt parallel in Turnus and Aeneas, pleasing to those who had also read the *Aeneid* but quite inappropriate to the distressed Egyptian damsel.

Marlowe was more successful in writing blank verse than the others, but even he could not keep a kind of shuttle rhythm out of his lines. He did not attempt to write blank verse as in any way representing normal speech : his aim was to be gorgeous and magnificent, to write in " high astounding terms " which suited the style of Alleyn and his company, who liked " sound and fury."

At first Shakespeare admired the current fashions.

He revelled in mere words, their sound, colour and glitter. He was at his best in Comedy and he liked rhyme, for he often moved more freely within the restraints of rhyme than in the freer blank verse. Comedy was still his natural outlet. It gave him the chance of choosing words and phrases with an ease and subtlety which, though this kind of cleverness has long passed out of fashion, no one else ever touched. It is shown at its best in *Love's Labour's Lost* in such a speech as the defence of " barbarism " which he gave to Berowne, a bubbling, many-coloured cascade of words. The thought is simple : that those who neglect everything for the sake of learning and never fall in love, miss more than they gain by their studies. In this speech he takes up the idea of light and darkness, to juggle with them in a dazzling display of verbal trickery :

" Why, all delights are vain, but that most vain
  Which, with pain purchased, doth inherit pain—
  As painfully to pore upon a book,
        To seek the light of truth, while truth the while
  Doth falsely blind the eyesight of his look :
        Light, seeking light, doth light of light beguile :
  So ere you find where light in darkness lies,
  Your light grows dark by losing of your eyes.
  Study me how to please the eye indeed,
        By fixing it upon a fairer eye,
  Who dazzling so, that eye shall be his heed,
        And give him light that it was blinded by.
  Study is like the heaven's glorious sun,
        That will not be deep-searched with saucy looks :

> Small have continual plodders ever won,
>   Save base authority from others' books.
> These earthly godfathers of heaven's lights,
>   That give a name to every fixed star,
> Have no more profit of their shining nights,
>   Than those that walk and wot not what they are.
> Too much to know, is to know nought but fame :
> And every godfather can give a name."

The four-fold " light," each with a slightly different meaning, in

> " Light, seeking light, doth light of light beguile,"

is an amazingly clever trick.

The outburst is neither profound thought nor good. drama, for everything must stand still until Berowne has finished. It is the sheer exuberance of an athlete who has discovered that he can play what game he likes with words. Yet the speech itself is significant. It is the answer of the " upstart crow " whose Latin was little and Greek less to those intellectual snobs who believed that all learning lived in books. Shakespeare's lack of book-learning was a blessing. When he needed a simile or an image he found it in his own experience and not in his reading.

In his early tragedies Shakespeare was less successful. He was still inclined to be heavy, especially when he wrote for effect. In *Richard III* Tyrrell describes the death of the little princes—an occasion for pathos and sentimentality :

" The tyrannous and bloody act is done ;
  The most arch deed of piteous massacre
  That ever yet this land was guilty of.
  Dighton and Forrest, whom I did suborn
  To do this piece of ruthless butchery,
  Albeit they were flesh'd villains, bloody dogs,
  Melting to tenderness and mild compassion,
  Wept like to children in their death's sad story.
  ' Oh ! thus,' quoth Dighton, ' lay the gentle babes : '
  ' Thus, thus,' quoth Forrest, ' girdling one another
  Within their alabaster innocent arms :
  Their lips were four red roses on a stalk,
  Which in their summer beauty kiss'd each other.
  A book of prayers on their pillow lay ;
  Which once,' quoth Forrest, ' almost chang'd my mind ;
  But, O, the devil '—there the villain stopp'd ;
  When Dighton told on : ' We smothered
  The most replenished sweet work of nature,
  That from the prime creation e'er she fram'd.'
  Hence both are gone with conscience and remorse ;
  They could not speak ; and so I left them both,
  To bear this tidings to the bloody king."

There is a sense of strain in the passage. Lines are hammered out to fit the pattern of the metre—

" That éver yét this lánd be gúilty óf."

Even the image of lips " like four red roses on a stalk " was pretty rather than apt, deliberately sentimental. The whole description is written for effect and is without real feeling : it is painted passion.

Shakespeare's earliest style is quite distinguishable. His rhythms are regular ; rhymes are common, used sometimes in alternate lines, more often in couplets. Occasionally he will even insert a sonnet into the dialogue. In the comedies there is much clever language, especially when young gentlemen are talking, which is sometimes trying, for wit changes its fashion quickly. There is excessive outpouring of " three-piled hyperboles " and imagery is often used for its own sake and not to clarify or intensify thought. In tragedy, and especially historical tragedy, Shakespeare was often bombastic and speeches were more heroic than suited the occasion. Shakespeare was still more interested in fine writing than in drama.

The best and the worst traits of his immature style are to be seen in the finest of his early plays, *Romeo and Juliet*. Lady Capulet urges Juliet to fall in love with Count Paris in a speech which for twelve lines plays with the far-fetched conceit that Paris is a book :

> " Read o'er the volume of young Paris' face,
> And find delight, writ there with beauty's pen,
> Examine every married lineament,
> And see how one another lends content :
> And what obscur'd in this fair volume lies,
> Find written in the margent of his eyes.
> This precious book of love, this unbound lover,
> To beautify him, only lacks a cover :
> The fish lives in the sea, and 'tis much pride
> For fair without the fair, within to hide :
> That book in many's eyes doth share the glory
> That in gold clasps locks in the golden story :
> So shall you share all that he doth possess,
> By having him, making yourself no less."

This is tediously clever.

Later Juliet, impatiently waiting for night and Romeo, breaks out into a lyric ecstasy which is just as elaborately poetical, but yet perfect :

" Gallop apace, you fiery-footed steeds,
Towards Phoebus' lodging, such a waggoner
As Phaethon would whip you to the west,
And bring in cloudy night immediately.
Spread thy close curtain, love-performing night,
That runaways eyes may wink, and Romeo
Leap to these arms, untalk'd of and unseen.
Lovers can see to do their amorous rites,
By their own beauties, or if love be blind,
It best agrees with night : come civil night,
Thou sober-suited matron all in black,
And learn me how to lose a winning match,
Play'd for a pair of stainless maidenhoods.
Hood my unmann'd blood baiting in my cheeks,
With thy black mantle, till strange love grow bold,
Think true love acted simple modesty :
Come night, come Romeo, come thou day in night,
For thou wilt lie upon the wings of night,
Whiter than new snow on a raven's back :
Come gentle night, come loving black-brow'd night,
Give me my Romeo, and when he shall die,
Take him and cut him out in little stars,
And he will make the face of heaven so fine,
That all the world will be in love with night,
And pay no worship to the garish Sun.
O I have bought the mansion of a love,
But not possess'd it, and though I am sold,
Not yet enjoy'd, so tedious is this day,
As is the night before some festival,
To an impatient child that hath new robes
And may not wear them."

The early style disappeared very rapidly as Shakespeare's experiences grew and with them his power of expression.

About two years later he wrote *The Merchant of Venice* (c. 1596). His serious dialogue was now better than his comic. Shylock expresses his hatred of Antonio plainly, clearly and passionately, for Shakespeare had entered into Shylock's mind and had felt his emotion :

> " Signior Antonio, many a time and oft
> In the Rialto have you rated me
> About my moneys and my usances :
> Still have I borne it with a patient shrug,
> (For sufferance is the badge of all our Tribe).
> You call me misbeliever, cut-throat dog,
> And spet upon my Jewish gabardine,
> And all for use of that which is mine own.
> Well then, it now appears you need my help :
> Go to then, you come to me, and you say,
> Shylock, we would have moneys, you say so :
> You that did void your rheum upon my beard,
> And foot me as you spurn a stranger cur
> Over your threshold, moneys is your suit.
> What should I say to you ?   Should I not say,
> Hath a dog money ? is it possible
> A cur can lend three thousand ducats ? or
> Shall I bend low, and in a bondman's key
> With bated breath, and whisp'ring humbleness,
> Say this : Fair sir, you spet on me on Wednesday last ;
> You spurn'd me such a day : another time
> You call'd me dog : and for these courtesies
> I'll lend you thus much moneys."

There is still just a trace of stiffness in the rhythm, a slight but perceptible pause at the end of each line, but not a superfluous word or unnecessary metaphor. Even Portia's set speech on " Mercy " in the Trial

Scene is appropriate in the occasion and the expression.

In the first part of *Henry IV*, written perhaps nine months later, Shakespeare was first completely master of his medium. This play has a wide range of very different characters, each skilfully contrasted, but each speaks in a language which in phrase, structure and rhythm is entirely appropriate. The most brilliant example of the contrast is in the scene where Hotspur, Glendower, Worcester and Mortimer compact their alliance. Shakespeare gained much by deliberate contrast. Hotspur, out of the ambition engendered in a hot head, cries out :

> " By heaven methinks it were an easy leap,
>   To pluck bright honour from the pale-fac'd moon,
>   Or dive into the bottom of the deep,
>   Where fadom-line could never touch the ground,
>   And pluck up drowned honour by the locks,
>   So he that doth redeem her thence might wear
>   Without corrival all her dignities,
>   But out upon this half-fac'd fellowship."

Falstaff, with the cynicism that comes from cold feet, grumbles :

> " 'Tis not due yet, I would be loath to pay him before his day, what need I be so forward with him that calls not on me ? Well, 'tis no matter, honour pricks me on ; yea, but how if honour prick me off when I come on ? how then ? Can honour set to a leg ? no, or an arm ? no, or take away the grief of a wound ? no. Honour hath no skill in surgery then ? no. What is honour ? a word. What is in that word honour ? what is that honour ? air. A trim reckoning. Who hath it ? he that died a' Wednesday. Doth he

feel it ? no. Doth he hear it ? no. 'Tis insensible then ? yea, to the dead. But will it not live with the living ? no. Why ? detraction will not suffer it, therefore I'll none of it. Honour is a mere scutcheon, and so ends my catechism."

The contrast enhances both speakers and speeches. Between *Henry IV* and *Hamlet* Shakespeare's technique developed rather than changed. There is not much in the dialogue or poetry of *Hamlet* that had not in some form appeared in earlier plays, but it is more competent, more supple. Each character, in long speeches or in conversation, not only speaks appropriately, but behind the words lies the whole compass of its particular personality and experience. This is seen in the less as well as the more important scenes. Thus, for instance, Hamlet having returned so dramatically to Denmark tells Horatio of his adventure on the ship which was to take him to England and to his destruction :

> " Up from my cabin
> My sea-gown scarf'd about me in the dark,
> Grop'd I to find out them ; had my desire,
> Finger'd their packet, and in fine, withdrew
> To mine own room again, making so bold,
> (My fears forgetting manners) to unseal
> Their grand commission, where I found, Horatio,
> Oh royal knavery : an exact command,
> Larded with many several sorts of reasons ;
> Importing Denmark's health, and England's too,
> With hoo, such bugs and goblins in my life,
> That on the supervise no leisure bated,
> No not to stay the grinding of the axe,
> My head should be struck off.

HORATIO : Is't possible ?

HAMLET : Here's the commission, read it at more leisure :
But wilt thou hear me how I did proceed ?

HORATIO : I beseech you.

HAMLET : Being thus be-netted round with villains,
Or I could make a prologue to my brains,
They had begun the play.   I sate me down,
Devis'd a new commission, wrote it fair,
I once did hold it as our statists do,
A baseness to write fair ; and labour'd much
How to forget that learning : but sir now,
It did me yeoman's service : wilt thou know
The effects of what I wrote ?

HORATIO : Ay, good my lord.

HAMLET : An earnest conjuration from the King,
As England was his faithful tributary,
As love between them, as the palm should flourish,
As Peace should still her wheaten garland wear,
And stand a comma 'tween their amities,
And many such-like As'es of great charge,
That on the view and know of these contents,
Without debatement further, more or less,
He should the bearers put to sudden death,
Not shriving-time allow'd."

In its place this speech is simply a piece of necessary information to explain how Hamlet came back. The description is vivid, but it is purely Hamlet's ; and, moreover, it shows a little more of Hamlet's own personality and experience : his youthful lessons in handwriting, the touch of conscious snobbery, his sardonic relish of the flowery pomposities of formal correspondence, his ruthlessness when roused.

The power of expression can be seen at its best in some of the soliloquies in Hamlet.   Soliloquy was an old device.   In modern stage conditions it always appears artificial, but it was common and appropriate in the intimacy of the Elizabethan playhouses.

In his earlier plays Shakespeare used it mainly for two purposes : to give information, or as an excuse for the recitation of a reflective poem.   Thus Richard III naively tells the audience that he is not indeed what he seems to others :

> " I do the wrong, and first begin to brawl.
> The secret mischiefs that I set abroach
> I lay unto the grievous charge of others.
> Clarence, whom I indeed, have cast in darkness,
> I do beweep to many simple gulls ;
> Namely, to Stanley, Hastings, Buckingham ;
> And tell them 'tis the queen and her allies
> That stir the king against the duke my brother.
> Now they believe it ; and withal whet me
> To be reveng'd on Rivers, Vaughan, Grey ;
> But then I sigh, and, with a piece of scripture,
> Tell them that God bids us do good for evil :
> And thus I clothe my naked villainy
> With odd old ends stol'n forth of holy writ,
> And seem a saint when most I play the devil."

Thus Richard II, alone in his prison, soliloquises leisurely on Life and Time in a poetical essay of sixty lines.

Hamlet also soliloquises ; in general reflection, as in his broodings over suicide—" To be or not to be " —but more often in passages which reveal also the movements of his mind, his perplexities and resolutions.   At times this revelation is so subtle that

Shakespeare shows not only Hamlet's mind working, but even the subconscious thought beneath.   After the play scene Claudius has rushed away, unable to conceal his guilt any longer.   He tries to pray.   As he is kneeling, Hamlet passes by.   He is keyed up for the murder that is to revenge his father.   He sees the unwitting King.   He feels that the supreme moment has come.   He moves towards the King :

" Now might I do it pat, [*drawing his sword*], now he is praying,
And now I'll do't [*approaching the King*], and so he goes to Heaven,
And so am I reveng'd : [*he poises to thrust.   The supreme moment has
        come.   He is about to take his revenge : but the word ' Heaven '
        echoes.   It is no vengeance to send Claudius to Heaven.   The
        moment, after all, is not fitting.   He lowers his point, and steps
        back*]   That would be scann'd
A villain kills my father, and for that,
I, his sole son, do this same villain send
To Heaven.
        [*He pauses the time of four stresses in silence as the thought takes
        root.   There comes back to his mind the murder which was to be
        avenged, and the Ghost's story, with its bitterest complaint
        ' Cut off even in the blossoms of my sins, unhousel'd, dis-
        appointed, unaneled, no reckoning made, but sent to my account
        with all my imperfections on my head.'   Death, here and now,
        would be a benefit to Claudius*]
He took my father grossly, full of bread,
With all his crimes broad blown, as flush as May,
And how his audit stands, who knows, save Heaven :
But in our circumstance and course of thought
'Tis heavy with him : and am I then reveng'd,
To take him in the purging of his soul,
When he is fit and season'd for his passage ?
No.
Up sword, and know thou a more horrid hent
When he is drunk asleep : or in his rage,
Or in th'incestuous pleasure of his bed,

At gaming, swearing, or about some act
That has no relish of salvation in't,
Then trip him, that his heels may kick at Heaven,
And that his soul may be as damn'd and black
As Hell, whereto it goes. [*Then with a final swirl of passion as he
    strides off*] My mother stays,
This physic but prolongs thy sickly days."

Othello, written some months later, is perhaps the most perfectly constructed of all Shakespeare's plays, and may best be used to illustrate the four different kinds of speech which he uses : lyric poetry, rhyme, blank verse, prose. All are used in *Othello* with the greatest artistry and to gain particular effects of tone, mood and atmosphere.

In Shakespeare's plays, and in Elizabethan drama generally, the general distinction between the use of prose and the use of blank verse is clear and simple. Prose dialogue keeps the scene down to the ordinary level of every day. The characters talk to each other with an easy naturalism. Blank verse heightens the atmosphere, giving dignity and emotion to the speakers. Certain persons naturally speak verse, others prose. Falstaff naturally speaks in prose, Hotspur in verse, whilst Prince Hal speaks prose in the company of Falstaff and verse to his father.

In *Othello* blank verse is the natural speech of Othello himself. He is a heroic and dignified person. Iago, on the other hand, is a lower character altogether. He speaks mostly in prose, but at times he breaks into verse, especially in his soliloquies when he is left to himself. Other prose characters do not. When Benedick or Falstaff come to soliloquise they speak in their natural medium, prose. But there is a distinct purpose in every change in Iago's speeches. They coincide with and express the subtle changes of his mood. Iago, the jocular, simple "honest Iago," speaks a quick prose. But Iago feigning honest indignation or expressing real hate is an emotional being; and verse, on the Elizabethan stage, is the natural expression of emotion. At his first entry in the beginning of the play he is seething with anger because Othello has rejected him and chosen Cassio. This is the real Iago speaking from his heart. His hate jets out in spasms of indignant rhetoric :

> " Despise me
>   If I do not. Three great ones of the City
>   (In personal suit to make me his Lieutenant)
>   Off-capp'd to him : and by the faith of man
>   I know my price, I am worth no worse a place.
>   But he (as loving his own pride and purposes)
>   Evades them, with a bumbast circumstance,
>   Horribly stuff'd with epithets of war,
>   And in conclusion,
>   Nonsuits my mediators. For certes, says he,
>   I have already chose my officer. And what was he ?
>   Forsooth, a great arithmetician,
>   One Michael Cassio, a Florentine,
>   (A fellow almost damn'd in a fair wife)
>   That never set a squadron in the field,
>   Nor the division of a battle knows
>   More than a spinster. Unless the bookish theoric :
>   Wherein the tongued Consuls can propose

As masterly as he. Mere prattle (without practice)
Is all his soldiership. But he, sir, had th'election ;
And I (of whom his eyes had seen the proof
At Rhodes, at Cyprus, and on other grounds,
Christian, and heathen), must be be-leed, and calm'd
By debitor, and creditor. This counter-caster,
He (in good time) must his Lieutenant be,
And I (God bless the mark) his Moorship's Ancient."

It is not until Brabantio also loses his temper that
Iago regains his self-control. Then once more he is
outwardly the mocker, speaking prose. After further, but milder, expression of his anger he goes out.
Next he appears in company with Othello. He is
now feigning indignation, and verse is the proper
medium for his speech.

In the scene in the Council Chamber Iago says
nothing, but watches. At the end he is left alone
with Roderigo. Again the mask is on and he speaks
a flippant, supple prose until Roderigo leaves him.
Then once more he is left alone and his real emotions
break out in powerful passionate verse, as the idea of
his plot begins to grow :

" How ? How ? Let's see.
After some time, to abuse Othello's ears,
That he is too familiar with his wife :
He hath a person, and a smooth dispose
To be suspected : fram'd to make women false.
The Moor is of a free, and open nature,
That thinks men honest, that but seem to be so,
And will as tenderly be led by th'nose
As asses are."

The rest of the line is silent, as the thought catches fire. Then with a little cry of triumph :

> " I have't : it is engender'd : Hell, and Night,
> Must bring this wondrous birth, to the world's light."

Thus by watching the speech used by Iago we have a subtle revelation of his outward manner. With Iago prose shows that the mask is on, that he is self-controlled, " honest " and frank. With Othello a lapse into prose denotes the opposite—a breakdown of control. Othello speaks prose only when he falls into his apoplectic fit and when he sees his handkerchief in Cassio's hand.

Another very good example of the different use of prose and verse occurs in the conversation between Desdemona and Emilia towards the end of the play. Othello has just gone out after his vile abuse of Desdemona. She suddenly asks :

> " Dost thou in conscience think (tell me Emilia)
> That there be women do abuse their husbands
> In such gross kind ?
>
> EMILIA : There be some such, no question.
> DESDEMONA : Wouldst thou do such a deed for all the world ?
> EMILIA : Why, would not you ?
> DESDEMONA : No, by this heavenly light.
> EMILIA : Nor I neither, by this heavenly light :
> I might as well do't i' th' dark.
> DESDEMONA : Wouldst thou do such a deed for all the world ?
> EMILIA : The world's a huge thing :
> It is a great price, for a small vice.
> DESDEMONA : In troth, I think thou wouldst not.

EMILIA : In troth I think I should, and undo't when I had done.
Marry, I would not do such a thing for a joint-ring, nor
for measures of lawn, nor for gowns, petticoats, nor
caps, nor any petty exhibition. But for the whole
world : 'uds pity, who would not make her husband
cuckold, to make him a monarch? I should venture
Purgatory for't."

Emilia for the moment is confused by Desdemona's
insistence and tries to turn it off in a laugh, but as
Desdemona still persists she evades her by regaining
her composure in indignant protestation—in rhetorical verse—against jealous husbands.

Shakespeare uses lyric verse to create a definite
atmosphere. It is always sung. There are two
notable examples in *Othello*. The first is in the
drinking scene, where Iago sings :

" And let me the canakin clink, clink :
And let me the canakin clink.
A soldier's a man : oh, man's life's but a span,
Why then let a soldier drink."

" King Stephen was and a worthy peer,
His breeches cost him but a crown,
He held them sixpence all too dear,
With that he call'd the tailor lown :
He was a wight of high renown,
And thou art but of low degree :
'Tis pride that pulls the country down,
Then take thy auld cloak about thee."

Both songs are sung loudly and create the atmosphere
of rowdy merriment which are the proper prelude
and mood for Cassio's drunkenness.

The second is the Willow song. After the dreadful scene where Othello treats Desdemona like a prostitute Shakespeare wishes to prepare our mood for the murder. So Desdemona sings very softly:

> " The poor soul sat sighing, by a sycamore tree.
> Sing all a green willow :
> Her hand on her bosom, her head on her knee,
> Sing willow, willow, willow.
> The fresh streams ran by her, and murmur'd her moans,
> Sing willow, willow, willow.
> Her salt tears fell from her, and soften'd the stones,
> Sing willow, willow, willow.
> Sing all a green willow must be my garland.
> Let nobody blame him, his scorn I approve.
>
> I call'd my love false love : but what said he then ?
> Sing, willow, willow, willow.
> If I court mo women, you'll couch with mo men."

The music has the same effect as a change of light in the modern theatre.

In *Othello* there is also a very notable instance of the use of rhyme. On the whole Shakespeare does not use much rhyme in his later plays. The rhymed couplet at the end of a scene was always liable to occur, but when he uses rhyme within a scene it is with a definite purpose. In the Council Chamber scene, after Brabantio has been humiliated by Desdemona's unexpected declaration of her love for Othello, the Duke tries to comfort him by lapsing into proverbs, or " sentences " as they were called :

" When remedies are past, the griefs are ended
  By seeing the worst, which late on hopes depended.
  To mourn a mischief that is past and gone,
  Is the next way to draw new mischief on.
  What cannot be preserv'd, when Fortune takes :
  Patience her injury a mock'ry makes.
  The robb'd that smiles, steals something from the thief,
  He robs himself, that spends a bootless grief."

Brabantio is irritated by these commonplaces, and retorts with a few proverbs of his own. Then, to point the contrast of mood, the Duke resumes not in blank verse, but in prose. Thus these two for the moment hold a kind of duet. As blank verse heightens speech and infuses it with emotion, so rhymed verse stiffens and gives it special emphasis. Here Shakespeare stressed the easy condolence of the man who was not touched by the sorrow of the inconsolable father. Then, as Brabantio goes out, he gives a parting message to Othello, which is both warning, prophecy, and curse :

" Look to her, Moor, if thou has eyes to see :
  She has deceiv'd her father, and may thee."

The rhymed couplet gives just the touch of oracular pronouncement necessary.

A few years later (1606) Shakespeare wrote *Lear* and *Macbeth*. To those who are not familiar with Shakespeare's language *Lear* is a difficult play to read because of its excessive concentration of thought. It is not so much that he uses a strange vocabulary or difficult words, as that he combines words and images to express thoughts which are in themselves almost beyond expression. The play itself was in some ways a new departure. He was concerned rather to show the significance of human conduct than to tell a dramatic story. What he wished to say could not be expressed in direct statement, but only by suggestion and flashes of meaning. As in his earlier plays, he was again consciously experimenting with language, but impatiently rather than joyously. He was no longer content with blank verse. He wrote speeches in great sweeps and not line by line, and even the formal pattern of five stresses was submerged in the rush of the whole. Moreover the imagery was no longer simple or direct but exceedingly complex, suggesting a dozen different ideas and associations in a sentence or two.

Edgar, disguised as the lunatic beggar, pauses in his flight to reflect on his own wretched state :

> " Yet better thus, and known to be contemn'd,
> Than still contemn'd and flatter'd, to be worst :
> The lowest and most dejected thing of Fortune,
> Stands still in esperance, lives not in fear :
> The lamentable change is from the best,
> The worst returns to laughter. Welcome then,
> Thou unsubstantial air that I embrace :
> The wretch that thou hast blown unto the worst,
> Owes nothing to thy blasts."

[He sees his father, now blinded and in agony, led by an old man.]

" But who comes here ?   My father poorly led ?
World, world, O world !
But that thy strange mutations make us hate thee,
Life would not yield to age."

Macbeth, shrinking from the murder of Duncan,
soliloquises :

" If it were done, when 'tis done, then 'twere well
It were done quickly : if th' assassination
Could trammel up the consequence, and catch
With his surcease, success : that but this blow
Might be the be-all, and the end-all.   Here,
But here, upon this bank and shoal of time,
We'ld jump the life to come.   But in these cases,
We still have judgement here, that we but teach
Bloody instructions, which being taught, return
To plague th' inventor.   This even-handed Justice
Commends th' ingredients of our poison'd chalice
To our own lips.   He's here in double trust ;
First, as I am his kinsman, and his subject,
Strong both against the deed : then, as his host,
Who should against his murderer shut the door,
Not bear the knife myself.   Besides, this Duncan
Hath borne his faculties so meek ; hath been
So clear in his great office, that his virtues
Will plead like angels, trumpet-tongu'd against
The deep damnation of his taking-off :
And Pity, like a naked new-born babe,
Striding the blast, or Heaven's cherubin, hors'd
Upon the sightless couriers of the air,
Shall blow the horrid deed in every eye,
That tears shall drown the wind.   I have no spur
To prick the sides of my intent, but only
Vaulting Ambition, which o'erleaps itself,
And falls on th' other.

The imagery is too thickly clotted for paraphrase
or analysis, but it expresses very adequately the
turmoil of Macbeth's mind.

In *Lear* Shakespeare uses certain words and ideas in all their meanings and associations to be, as it were, the theme words of the story. They are *Nature* and *Nothing*. Lear, in his foolish optimism, regards the filial duty of affection as natural. When Cordelia offends him he casts her out as " a wretch whom Nature is ashamed almost to acknowledge hers." Later, when Goneril offends him, he curses her, calling on Nature to suspend her purpose : either to make Goneril childless, or, if she must have a child, that it may be " a thwart disnatured torment to her." Goneril and Regan he regards as " unnatural hags," but in the end Cordelia " redeems Nature from the general curse " that should follow her sisters' evil deeds.

Edmund the Bastard, the "natural" son of Gloucester, begotten " in the lusty stealth of Nature," dedicates himself to her :

> " Thou Nature art my Goddess, to thy Law
> My services are bound."

for Nature is the Goddess of ruthless selfishness. " Loyal and natural boy," Gloucester calls him, with grim unconscious irony. Shakespeare uses " nature," " natural," " naturally," forty-seven times in *Lear*. The words become a sinister echo throughout the play.

The word " nothing " likewise is terribly significant. Cordelia, when her turn comes to praise her father and so justify his favouritism, is tongue-tied and can utter only " Nothing, my Lord."

" Nothing ? " echoes Lear.

" Nothing."

" Nothing will come of nothing, speak again."

Lear is wrong, for from this " nothing " comes everything. The word echoes in the parallel story of Gloucester, also mistaking the loyalty of his children.

" What paper were you reading ? " he asks, as Edmund ostentatiously conceals the false letter which is to ruin Edgar.

He too replies, " Nothing, my Lord," and again from " nothing " follows everything.

Antony and Cleopatra, if the accepted date (1607) is correct, followed *Lear* by some months. It lacks the vastness of *Lear*. Shakespeare was not consciously experimenting with this new technique of verse, but he had learnt much : he had developed new muscles. The theme did not allow for the titanic treatment of *Lear*, but the story, as Plutarch told it, called up in him an enthusiasm which he certainly did not feel in *Julius Caesar*, to which *Antony and Cleopatra* was the sequel.

In the verse of *Antony and Cleopatra* there is a kind of resonance which he achieved nowhere else : it has a deep beauty quite its own. This quality comes out again and again in some haunting phrase or echo which exists in the sound of the words themselves, quite apart from their context :

> " Oh, my oblivion is a very Antony,
> And I am all forgotten."

The exact meaning does not matter : it is a lovely sound in itself.

But poetry does not live by sound alone : it needs also perfect aptness of meaning. The finest example in the play is the description of Antony's first meeting with Cleopatra, which Shakespeare, with superb instinct, put into the mouth of the cynic Enobarbus, when his friends at Rome are trying to get from him the latest Cleopatra scandal. Here Shakespeare reverted to a piece of sheer description, of a kind that he had not allowed himself for years. His imagination was obviously kindled to write it by the gorgeous original in North's *Plutarch*, which was in itself a rich piece of prose. He held up the play that Enobarbus might describe the event, and in such a way that it might explain, what was otherwise inexplicable, Cleopatra's power of fascinating Antony.

> " I will tell you.
> The barge she sat in, like a burnish'd Throne
> Burnt on the water : the poop was beaten gold,
> Purple the sails : and so perfumed that
> The winds were love-sick.
> With them the oars were silver,
> Which to the tune of flutes kept stroke, and made
> The water which they beat, to follow faster ;

As amorous of their strokes. For her own person,
It beggar'd all description, she did lie
In her pavilion, cloth-of-gold, of tissue,
O'er-picturing that Venus, where we see
The fancy outwork Nature. On each side her,
Stood pretty dimpled boys, like smiling Cupids,
With divers-colour'd fans whose wind did seem,
To glow the delicate cheeks which they did cool,
And what they undid did . . .

Her gentlewomen, like the Nereides,
So many mermaids tended her i' th' eyes,
And made their bends adornings. At the helm,
A seeming mermaid steers : the silken tackle,
Swell with the touches of those flower-soft hands,
That yarely frame the office. From the barge
A strange invisible perfume hits the sense
Of the adjacent wharfs. The city cast
Her people out upon her : and Antony
Enthron'd i' th' market-place, did sit alone,
Whistling to th' air : which but for vacancy,
Had gone to gaze on Cleopatra too,
And made a gap in Nature . . .

Upon her landing, Antony sent to her,
Invited her to supper : she replied,
It should be better, he became her guest :
Which she entreated, our courteous Antony,
Whom ne'er the word of no woman heard speak,
Being barber'd ten times o'er, goes to the feast ;
And for his ordinary, pays his heart,
For what his eyes eat only. . . .

I saw her once
Hop forty paces through the public street,
And having lost her breath, she spoke, and panted,
That she did make defect, perfection,
And breathless power breathe forth.
MAECENAS : Now Antony must leave her utterly.

ENOBARBUS : Never he will not :
        Age cannot wither her, nor custom stale
        Her infinite variety : other women cloy
        The appetites they feed, but she makes hungry,
        Where most she satisfies.   For vilest things
        Become themselves in her, that the holy Priests
        Bless her, when she is riggish."

Apart from the sheer magnificence of the speech, it was not a mere bravery—Shakespeare showing off his powers as in the Queen Mab speech in *Romeo and Juliet* or Berowne's speech in *Love's Labour's Lost*. Nor was it only an orchestral setting for Cleopatra. It is, in anticipation, part of the music of Cleopatra's death ; and it comes back at the end as an echo :

    " Show me my women like a Queen : go fetch
      My best attires.   I am again for Cydnus,
      To meet Mark Antony."

In death as in life

    " Age cannot wither her, nor custom stale
      Her infinite variety."

And indeed the poetry of the play is full of echoes :

    " Let Rome in Tiber melt, and the wide arch
      Of the rang'd Empire fall : here is my space,
      Kingdoms are clay : our dungy earth alike
      Feeds beast as man ; the nobleness of life
      Is to do thus : when such a mutual pair,
      And such a twain can do't, in which I bind
      On pain of punishment, the world to weet
      We stand up peerless."

Thus Antony in his moment of triumphant love. And the echo comes back later from Cleopatra, alone and deserted,—

> " My desolation does begin to make
> A better life : 'tis paltry to be Caesar :
> Not being Fortune, he's but Fortune's knave,
> A minister of her will : and it is great
> To do that thing that ends all other deeds,
> Which shackles accidents, and bolts up change ;
> Which sleeps, and never palates more the dung,
> The beggar's nurse, and Caesar's.''

And again, Antony nearing his end :

> " Unarm Eros, the long day's task is done,
> And we must sleep."

This is echoed by Iras to Cleopatra :

> " Finish, good Lady, the bright day is done,
> And we are for the dark."

It is an echo and a contrast. To Antony, the long day meant work, and then rest : to Cleopatra brilliance. She must shine or go out.

There is another note in the incomparable music of this play : its changes of mood, tone and pace. As a modern producer gains effects of change and contrast by lighting and music, so Shakespeare changed the atmosphere of his scenes by contrasts of verse, tone and speed. In Act IV Scene xii there is a scene of battle. Antony is defeated. He enters raging against Cleopatra. She comes to him. He drives her away with fury and cursing. She reappears for a moment and runs off terrified by his wrath. And then, the fury exhausted and the passion spent, Antony returns with his servant Eros.

ANTONY : Eros, thou yet behold'st me ?
EROS : Ay noble Lord.
ANTONY : Sometime we see a cloud that's dragonish,
    A vapour sometime, like a bear, or lion,
    A tower'd citadel, a pendent rock,
    A forked mountain, or blue promontory
    With trees upon't, that nod unto the world,
    And mock our eyes with air.
    Thou hast seen these signs,
    They are black Vesper's pageants.
EROS : Ay my Lord.
ANTONY : That which is now a horse, even with a thought
    The rack dislimns, and makes it indistinct
    As water is in water.

Antony, like the swan, is dying to slow music :

        So it must be, for now
    All length is torture : since the torch is out,
    Lie down and stray no farther.   Now all labour
    Mars what it does : yea, very force entangles
    Itself with strength : seal then and all is done.

Between *Coriolanus* (c. 1607–8) and *Cymbeline* (c. 1610) there was apparently a period when Shakespeare wrote little.   Then in 1610 and 1611 he wrote *Cymbeline, The Winter's Tale* and *The Tempest. Cymbeline* has few admirers.   It is an astonishing decline from the level of a few years previously. *The Winter's Tale*, in its dialogue, is Shakespeare at his best, though the structure of the play, awkwardly broken by an interval of sixteen years between Acts III and IV, is unequal. In *The Tempest* he achieved what some competent critics regard as his final and greatest play. In its poetry Shakespeare reached the farthest limits possible to the English language in expression and solemn music. The thought is still packed, but no longer obscure, the verse free but perfectly controlled. The English language, unlike Latin, is not suited for precise utterance : it has too many little monosyllables which are necessary to modify its meanings. A Roman could express in a single word every mood and tense of love by conjugating " amo." An Englishman must add his " I would " or " I might have been." Shakespeare in *The Tempest* showed what could be done, even with English.

In the later speeches he reached his final mastery over words. The meaning is clear, the thought deep, the emotional music perfect :

> " You do look, my son, in a mov'd sort,
> As if you were dismay'd : be cheerful sir,
> Our revels now are ended : these our actors
> (As I foretold you) were all spirits, and
> Are melted into air, into thin air,
> And like the baseless fabric of this vision
> The cloud-capp'd Towers, the gorgeous Palaces,
> The solemn Temples, the great Globe itself,
> Yea, all which it inherit, shall dissolve,
> And like this insubstantial pageant faded
> Leave not a rack behind : we are such stuff
> As dreams are made on ; and our little life

Is rounded with a sleep : sir, I am vex'd,
Bear with my weakness, my old brain is troubled :
Be not disturb'd with my infirmity,
If you be pleas'd, retire into my cell,
And there repose : a turn or two, I'll walk
To still my beating mind."

There will doubtless come a time when this prophecy is fulfilled ; but until the English language in its turn has perished, in *The Tempest* lies its greatest achievement.

CHAPTER VIII

EDITING SHAKESPEARE

WHEN Shakespeare died in 1616 only fourteen of his plays were regularly in print, namely : *Richard III, Titus Andronicus, Love's Labour's Lost, Romeo and Juliet, A Midsummer Night's Dream, Richard II, Merchant of Venice, Henry IV* (Part 1), *Henry IV* (Part II), *Much Ado About Nothing, Troilus and Cressida, Hamlet, Lear, Pericles.* *Othello* was printed in 1622, and pirated Quartos of *Romeo and Juliet, Henry V, Merry Wives of Windsor* and *Hamlet* had also appeared. The rest of his plays were first printed in 1623, when his surviving friends produced a collection in one volume known as the First Folio : it included also all the plays already printed, with the exception of *Pericles.*

In all Shakespeare's texts there are difficulties of reading and interpretation due to errors in printing. Sometimes the misprints are obvious ; sometimes phrases and sentences are quite unintelligible. To make the text smooth and readable some tidying is necessary, particularly as Shakespeare apparently did not prepare his plays for printing. They were originally intended as scripts for actors and not as texts for readers. Scholars have therefore edited the texts, that is, have made alterations and additions to the originals to make them more intelligible and easy for the reader.

Until about twenty years ago the original texts, Quarto or Folio, were not highly regarded. Editors believed that Elizabethan printers were careless, ignorant men, who knew little of the refinements of literature, and could never be relied on to reproduce accurately the copy before them. Hence an edited text was preferable to an original.

Modern scholars, as the result of the exact study of Elizabethan texts, have established certain principles.

The most important authority for any text must be the author's own manuscript. No play manuscript used by a printer during Shakespeare's lifetime has survived.

The next most important text must be that printed directly from the manuscript. The earliest surviving text is therefore the most reliable, unless, either a later text is based on a better original, or a later edition was revised by the author.

This sometimes happened with Shakespeare's plays. The first edition of *Hamlet* was a very bad pirated Quarto which came out in 1603 ; the second Quarto, dated 1604, was probably printed from Shakespeare's own manuscript, and is thus the better text.

When a play is constantly reprinted and changes

of reading occur in later editions they are usually due to later editing and therefore of little value.

Nor was Elizabethan printing so haphazard as was formerly supposed ; rather it differed in principle from modern usage and especially in matters of spelling, use of capitals and italic, and punctuation.

Even now, although English spelling is largely fixed, there are considerable minor differences in practice between the various printing and publishing houses. One firm, for instance, refuses to allow its authors to use an " s " in *civilization* or at the end of " *northward*." Few English authors are really expert in spelling, punctuation or even the exact niceties of grammar, as they soon learn when a professional proof-reader has gone over their manuscript.

The history of the Elizabethan stage-play from the time when its author first sharpened his quill till it reaches a modern reprint is often very complicated ; and particularly in the early part of Shakespeare's career, when as yet neither actors nor dramatists regarded plays as literature. Henslowe's *Diary*, especially between the years 1598 and 1602, gives the most valuable information. At this time Henslowe was acting as a banker to the players and made payments on their behalf to playwrights. These payments show how plays were written.

Most of the plays acted at his theatres were put together by syndicates of two, three and sometimes even five writers. Playwriting was thus a practical business rather than high art. In 1598, for instance, Henry Chettle collaborated in the writing of twelve plays and made alterations in three others. In 1599 Thomas Dekker wrote two plays by himself and collaborated in fourteen. It may be worth noting that of the two-hundred-and-eighty plays mentioned by Henslowe about one in seven survives, and these are mostly the work of a single author. It was only natural that an author should be more interested in his own work and so take steps to have it printed ; and that the creation of a single mind should be of greater artistic value.

The Diary also shows that popular plays were often revised with alterations and additions. Thus Marlowe's Tragedy of Dr. Faustus, one of the most popular Elizabethan plays, was first written in 1592. Henslowe recorded twenty-five performances between September 1594 and October 1597. It was entered for publication on 7th January, 1601. Bird and Rowley, two of Henslowe's hacks, were paid for making additions to the play on the 22nd November, 1602. The earliest surviving quarto of the play (which is probably not the first edition, and a pirated text, at that), is dated 1604. A fourth quarto dated 1616 has considerable alterations and additions ; and in a ninth quarto of 1663 there are still further changes.

Revision and collaboration are thus present in many Elizabethan plays, and as soon as Shakespeare's plays are closely examined, it is clear that they too have sometimes been altered and revised. Collaboration in a printed play can be detected only by style, and editors are seldom agreed on matters of style. There is, however, fairly general agreement that portions of *Macbeth*, particularly the Bloody Sergeant's Speech in Act I Scene ii and the Hecate scenes in Act III Scene v and Act IV Scene i, are not by Shakespeare. Collaboration would also explain the unevenness in *King John*.

Revision is obvious in the early texts of *Hamlet*, *Romeo and Juliet*, and *Love's Labour's Lost*. In the Second Quarto of *Hamlet* there are 218 lines which do not appear in the Folio and in the Folio 85 lines which do not appear in the Quarto. In the early Quartos of *Love's Labour's Lost* and of *Romeo and Juliet* there are instances where both the original and the revised version of a speech are printed. In the Second Quarto of *Romeo and Juliet* (1599) the last lines of Romeo's final speech, Act V Scene iii, are printed thus :

> " Ah deare *Iuliet*
> Why art thou yet so faire ?   I will beleeue,
> Shall I beleeue that vnsubstantiall death is amorous,
> And that the leane abhorred monster keepes
> Thee here in darke to be his parramour ?
> For feare of that I still will staie with thee,
> And neuer from this pallat of dym night
> Depart againe, come lye thou in my arme,
> Heer's to thy health, where ere thou tumblest in.
> O true Appothecarie !
> Thy drugs are quicke.   Thus with a kisse I die.

Depart againe, here, here, will I remaine,
With wormes that are thy Chamber-maides : O here
Will I set vp my euerlasting rest :
And shake the yoke of inauspicious starres,
From this world wearied flesh, eyes looke your last :
Armes take your last embrace : And lips, O you
The doores of breath, feale with a righteous kisse
A datelesse bargaine to ingrossing death :
Come bitter conduct, come vnsauoury guide,
Thou desperate Pilot, now at once run on
The dashing Rocks, thy seasick weary barke :
Heeres to my Loue.   O true Appothecary :
Thy drugs are quicke.   Thus with a kisse I die."

In modern texts the lines repeated have been
omitted.   It is clear that Shakespeare rewrote and
expanded the speech ; but the printer misunder-
stood his copy and printed both the old and new
ending.

It follows that every play must be carefully examined by itself to see whether there are any signs
of its history.   In general the history of a play
manuscript is this.   The author (or authors) having
written the play delivered the manuscript to the
company.   The prompter then read it over and
prepared it for performance by adding the necessary
notes of the stage business and the like.   The
individual actors' parts were copied out with the
cues.   Amongst the Dulwich papers there still survives Alleyn's part as Orlando in Greene's *Orlando
Furioso*.   The play manuscript was then sent to the
Master of Revels to be censored and licensed.   The
play was rehearsed and acted, and the manuscript

was used in the theatre as a prompt-copy. When the play had passed out of the repertory the manuscript might be sold to a printer.

In many instances the text which reached the printer was the author's original manuscript. Towards the end of Shakespeare's career, however, when literary gentlemen liked to possess plays in their libraries, play manuscripts were copied out by professional copyists. There were good reasons for keeping the number of copies as low as possible, because as yet there was no dramatic copyright. The manuscript of a popular play might thus have been constantly altered and revised before it reached the printer, passages for omission being marked or scored through, and new additions being pasted or pinned in. It was easy for confusion and errors to arise.

All these processes can be illustrated from one of the few manuscripts of an Elizabethan stage-play which still exist. The manuscript is in the British Museum and is known as *The Book of Sir Thomas More*. It is a chronicle play of the usual type, showing scenes in the life and death of More. The manuscript is written in seven different handwritings ; it has been revised and enlarged but apparently was never printed or played. Most of the play is in the handwriting of Antony Munday, but there are additions in other handwritings which have been labelled Hands A, B, C, D and E. Of these, Hand E is

Thomas Dekker's and Hand C the Playhouse Reviser's of the Rose Theatre.

The manuscript also bears the observations and orders of Edmund Tilney, Master of the Revels, who censored it heavily because of the political significance of some of the speeches in the crowd and riot scenes. He sent the manuscript back with the note " leave out the insurrection wholly and begin with Sir Thomas More at the Mayor's sessions with a report afterwards of his good service done, as Shreve of London upon a mutiny against the Lombards, only by a short report and not otherwise at your perils."

Such a manuscript is in itself of great interest, but the more so, since Hand D, which contributed three autographed pages in a scene showing Sir Thomas More haranguing a crowd of riotous citizens, is believed to be Shakespeare's. The case was argued at length in *Shakespeare's Hand and Sir Thomas More*, edited by Professor A. W. Pollard.

The evidence is of three kinds : handwriting, spelling and poetry.

The evidence from the handwriting is the least conclusive. Very little of Shakespeare's handwriting remains. Apart from some disputable specimens, only six undoubted signatures survive and the words By me. There is nothing remarkable in this lack of Shakespeare's autographs. Nothing at all survives of Greene or Marlowe's writing, and of all the manuscripts used by Elizabethan printers during

Shakespeare's lifetime there only survives one half of one. From handwriting alone it is not possible to say definitely whether Shakespeare did or did not write the Three Pages, which, however, are not in the handwriting of any other known dramatist.

The evidence from spelling is stronger. In the good Quartos of Shakespeare's plays, which were probably set up from his own manuscript, certain unusual spellings occur. The Elizabethan compositor was free and easy with spelling, but already a conventional spelling was beginning and certain spellings are rare in printed books. The printer would usually normalise an unconventional spelling ; he would not make usual spelling abnormal. It is likely, therefore, that the curious spellings in the Quartos derive from Shakespeare's own manuscript. In the Three Pages also certain letters are carelessly made and easily misread, especially *d* and *e* (which in Elizabethan handwriting are similar though of different size), and the " minim " letters—*u* (which was also used for *v*), *m*, *n*, *i* (also used for *j*).

Many of the misprints in the Quartos were due to confusion in the " minim " letters ; thus *five*, written *fiue*, could easily be misread as *fine* or *find*. The argument from spelling, though striking, is not conclusive because as yet no one has undertaken a large and comprehensive study of Elizabethan spelling in general.

The literary evidence is the strongest. The crowd

scenes in *Sir Thomas More* can be paralleled closely with other crowd scenes in Shakespeare's own plays : the Jack Cade scenes in *Henry VI*, the forum scene in *Julius Caesar* and the crowd scenes in *Coriolanus*. The speech itself is similar in sentiment and rhythm to the great speech of Ulysses on degree in *Troilus and Cressida*. The principal speech in the Three Pages reads in a modernised version :

> " Nay, certainly you are ;
> For to the King God hath His office lent
> Of dread, of justice, power and command,
> Hath bid him rule, and will'd you to obey ;
> And, to add ampler majesty to this,
> He hath not only lent the King His figure,
> His throne and sword, but given him His own Name,
> Calls him a god on earth.   What do you, then,
> Rising 'gainst him that God Himself installs,
> But rise 'gainst God ?   What do you to your souls
> In doing this ?   O desperate as you are,
> Wash your foul minds with tears, and those same hands,
> That you like rebels lift against the peace,
> Lift up for peace, and your unreverent knees,
> Make them your feet to kneel to be forgiven !
> Tell me but this : what rebel captain,
> As mutinies are incident, by his name
> Can still the rout ?   Who will obey a traitor ?
> Or how can well that proclamation sound,
> When there is no addition but a rebel
> To qualify a rebel ?   You'll put down strangers,
> Kill them, cut their throats, possess their houses,
> And lead the majesty of law in liom,
> To slip him like a hound.   Say now th' king
> (As he is clement, if the offender mourn)
> Should so much come too short of your great trespass
> As but to banish you, whither would you go ?
> What country, by the nature of your error,

Should give you harbour ?   Go you to France or Flanders,
To any German province, Spain or Portugal,
Nay, anywhere that not adheres to England,—
Why, you must needs be strangers ; would you be pleased
To find a nation of such barbarous temper,
That, breaking out in hideous violence,
Would not afford you an abode on earth,
Whet their detested knives against your throats,
Spurn you like dogs, and like as if that God
Owed not nor made not you, nor that the elements
Were not all appropriate to your comforts,
But chartered unto them, what would you think
To be thus used ?   This is the strangers' case ;
And this your momtanish inhumanity."

In the manuscript, the speech is spelt and punctuated thus :

" Nay certainly you ar
    for to the king god hath his offyc lent
    of dread of iustyce, power and comaund
    hath bid him rule, and willd you to obay
    and to add ampler maiestie to this
    he hath not only lent the king his figure
    his throne and sword, but gyven him his owne name
    calls him a god on earth, what do you then
    rysing gainst him that god himsealf enstalls
    but ryse gainst god, what do you to your sowles
    in doing this o desperat as you are.
    wash your foule mynds with teares and those same hands
    that you lyke rebells lyft against the peace
    lift vp for peace, and your vnreuerent knees
    make them your feet to kneele to be forgyven ;
    tell me but this what rebell cáptaine
    as mutynes ar incident, by his name
    can still the rout who will obay a traytor
    or howe can well that proclamation sounde
    when ther is no adicion but a rebell
    to quallyfy a rebell, youle put downe straingers

kill them cutt their throts possesse their howses
and leade the maiestie of law in liom
to slipp him lyke a hound ; say nowe the king
as he is clement, yf thoffendor moorne
shoold so much com to short of your great trespas
as but to banysh you, whether woold you go.
what country by the nature of your error
shoold gyve you harber go you to France or Flanders
to any Iarman province, Spane or Portigall
nay any where that not adheres to Ingland
why you must needs be straingers, woold you be pleasd
to find a nation of such barbarous temper
that breaking out in hiddious violence
woold not afoord you, an abode on earth
whett their detested knyves against your throtes
spurne you lyke doggs, and lyke as yf that god
owed not nor made not you, nor that the elaments
wer not all appropriat to your comforts.
but charterd vnto them, what woold you thinck
to be thus vsd, this is the straingers case
and this your momtanish inhumanyty.

The case is not yet finally proved, as there are
several flaws in the original argument. The authors
of *Shakespeare's Hand* assigned the play to the year
1594 or thereabouts ; but Shakespeare could not have
written the passage so early, for he did not develop
so competent and fluent a style until at least five
years later. A good case has, however, been made
for the year 1601. If so, the passages which so
disturbed Edmund Tilney were sentiments which
might have been taken to refer to the rebellion of
the Earl of Essex, and the style is consistent with
other plays which Shakespeare wrote at this time.

The study of this manuscript has led to the founding of a new principle of textual criticism : that when an editor proposes to emend a text which he suspects to be corrupt, he must take into account the author's handwriting. If his proposed emendation is not due to a probable misreading, then it is to be suspected. This is the principle adopted by Professor Dover Wilson in the *New Shakespeare*, which is sometimes called " scientific bibliography."

Actually, it is neither so scientific nor so infallible as it sounds. The editor has not seen the original manuscript ; he can only guess what its appearance might have been. Even if it were possible to guess what the printer saw before him in his copy, the editor must also guess what the printer knew. Most men who write fast and not too legibly produce in their manuscripts words which are not in themselves clear ; but the reader, knowing something of the matter in hand, can guess the meaning from the context. In a private letter there is usually not much difficulty. When, however, a manuscript is passed to a printer who knows little of the subject and is not particularly interested by it, he will guess the illegible words ; and his guess will depend on his education and experience. Anyone who has had to deal considerably with printers and typists will have experienced this. The ignorant typist, unable to read her copy, will cheerfully produce nonsense ; the second-class typist will not be content with nonsense, but will make a sense of her own. The perfect secretary will make a correct copy because she is familiar with the matter.

My own experience of printers (which is now considerable) has shaken my first faith in scientific bibliography. The most striking instance occurred in a short introduction for an edition of Marston's *Malcontent*. Contrary to usual (and wiser) practice, a manuscript copy was sent to the printer. The proof returned with twenty-four errors in two thousand words—an unusually large proportion. Some of these errors were so striking that at first glance it seemed a telling confirmation of the value of " scientific bibliography," but on comparing the proof with the original manuscript it worked the other way. Of the twenty-four errors only ten were due to mis-reading of the handwriting. For some the printer could not be held responsible : *Maeilente* for *Macilente*, *Lampateo* for *Lampatho* ; *servants* for *seruants*. Others were possible misreadings of the script but made no sense in their context, as *make* for *unable*, *that* for *but*, *pave* for *grave*. The remainder were of the printer's own unaided making, such as *folies* for *follies*, *devision*, *reconizable*, *Johnson* for *Jonson* (twice), *John* for *Ihon* (in a quoted title page), *Parles Churchyard* for *Paul's Churchyard*. Three were particularly striking. I was made to speak of a character called *Tharsicles* in a play of *Troilus and Creosida*, and, most interesting of all, " they [Marston's satires] pil-loried many recognisable contemporaries " became (the printer's mind having strayed from Marston to a motor-cycle for two) they "pillioned." Of the twenty-four errors, less than half were due to the copy.

These errors were a revelation of the printer's mind. Obviously he was bored with the matter and never gave a thought either to context or meaning. Nor was he used to literary copy. Had he known even the names of Shakespeare's plays he would have associated *Troilus* rather with *Cressida* than with *creosote* ; he would have known that Ben's surname was spelt without an *h*.

The handwriting of an author is only one of many causes of error in the printed text, for at times printers will make the oddest mistakes even when following printed copy. There is indeed no accounting for a large proportion of human errors.[1]

As has been seen, only a small proportion of Elizabethan plays was ever published ; most of them have perished. The players objected to the publication of plays for practical reasons, but as the standard improved, so there grew up a literary interest in plays. It set the fashion amongst literary-minded gentlemen to read plays and to collect them

[1] Amongst other misprints which have come my way, the following is worth note. In a book on the Earl of Essex I wrote " ' *Well*,' sighed Essex, ' *it may be so*.' " The printer inexplicably produced " ' *Gos* ', sighed Essex, ' *it may be so*.' " Hereupon the proof-reader wrote in the margin : "*Query* : ' *Gosh* ' ?"

in their libraries. Lord Mountjoy's secretary noted one of his recreations as reading play-books. Sir John Harington in 1610 possessed 129 play-books, and during the years 1600-10 he bought 90 out of 105 which were published during those years.[1] It became also a practice for certain authors to make a second copy of their plays and sell it to the printers, though this was considered hardly honest.

Sometimes play manuscripts were stolen, or if a play was particularly popular or topical some hack would be paid to vamp up a pirated copy. The pirated texts of Henry V, Hamlet, and The Merry Wives of Windsor were produced in this way. Sometimes when the players were hard up they sold their play-books. After the dislocation caused by the plague of 1592-4, twenty-two plays were published in one year. When a play had ceased to be profitable, it was sometimes sold; and there were occasions when for some particular reason it was desirable to allow printed copies to be circulated. Thus the Lord Chamberlain's Men allowed the first part of Henry IV to be published, probably to demonstrate to the world that Oldcastle's name had been changed to Falstaff.[2]

Although the players had no dramatic copyright in their plays, they were not without some protection. There was a printers' copyright; a printer,

---

[1] *Elizabethan Stage*, iii, p. 183.
[2] *See p. 79.*

INTRODUCING SHAKESPEARE

by the rules of the Stationers' Company, was obliged
to enter the titles of books which he printed in
the Stationers' Register. This gave him sole right
to print. In practice, however, printers were very
casual in observing the regulations, and only about
two-thirds of the books printed were actually
entered. Books were not allowed to be entered
unless the authority of the wardens of the Stationers'
Company, or of the Archbishop of Canterbury or
the Bishop of London or the Privy Council, had first
been secured. Players were sometimes able to
prevent the unwarranted printing of their plays by
appealing to their patrons. Sometimes they arranged
with a printer to enter the play in the Stationers'
Register and so secure copyright, but with no
intention of printing it.

Elizabethan play-texts were often carelessly printed. Some authors, such as Ben Jonson, who had a
high opinion of their own works, carefully super-
vised the printing, but most plays show little sign of
editing or preparation for the press. The spelling
is more erratic than in most Elizabethan books ;
there are no place-headings at the beginnings of
scenes ; the scenes are seldom marked, and often
there is even no division into Acts. The punctuation
is dramatical rather than grammatical. The punctuation in the Quartos is usually much lighter than in
the Folio, and it is always worth careful note. Play
manuscripts were punctuated to show how the

speech should be pronounced, but in most of the Folio texts it has been very carefully revised.

It is surprising how varying texts can differ from each other in small particulars. The simplest way of following this is to set alongside the same passage as it occurs in succeeding versions. The passage chosen is from the last Act of *Hamlet*, when Hamlet and Laertes begin the fencing match. The texts are : A. The Second Quarto of 1604 ; B. The First Folio of 1623 ; C. Nathaniel Rowe's edition of 1709 ; D. The standard Oxford edition dated 1928 ; E. The new Cambridge *Shakespeare*, 1934.

INTRODUCING SHAKESPEARE

A

King. Set me the stoopes of wine vpon that table,
If *Hamlet* giue the first or second hit,
Or quit in answere of the third exchange,
Let all the battlements their ordnance fire.
The King shall drinke to *Hamlets* better breath,
And in the cup an Vnice shall he throwe,
Richer then that which foure successiue Kings
In Denmarkes Crowne haue worne : giue me the cups,
And let the kettle to the trumpet speake,
The trumpet to the Cannoneere without,
The Cannons to the heauens, the heauen to earth.
Now the King drinkes to *Hamlet*, come beginne.   *Trumpets*
And you the Iudges beare a wary eye.   *the while.*

   Ham. Come on sir.
   Laer. Come my Lord.
   Ham. One.
   Laer. No.
   Ham. Iudgement.
   Ostrick. A hit, a very palpable hit.   *Drum, trumpets and shot.*
   Laer. Well, againe.   *Florish, a peece goes off.*
   King. Stay, giue me drinke, *Hamlet* this pearle is thine.
Heeres to thy health : giue him the cup.
   Ham. Ile play this bout first, set it by a while
Come, another hit.   What say you ?
   Laer. I doe confest.
   King. Our sonne shall winne.
   Quee. Hee's fat and scant of breath.
Heere *Hamlet* take my napkin rub thy browes,
The Queene carowses to thy fortune *Hamlet.*
   Ham. Good Madam.
   King. Gertrard doe not drinke.
   Quee. I will my Lord, I pray you pardon me.
   King. It is the poysned cup, it is too late.

From the Second Quarto of 1604. This text wa probably set up from Shakespeare's own manuscript. Note the spellings " Vnice," " Cannoneere," " Ostrick," " Gertrard," " poysned."

B

King. Set me the Stopes of wine vpon that Table:
If *Hamlet* giue the first, or second hit,
Or quit in answer of the third exchange,
Let all the Battlements their Ordinance fire,
The King shal drinke to *Hamlets* better breath,
And in the Cup an vnion shal he throw
Richer then that, which foure successiue Kings
In Denmarkes Crowne haue worne.
Giue me the Cups,
And let the Kettle to the Trumpets speake,
And Trumpet to the Cannoneer without,
The Cannons to the Heauens, the Heauen to Earth,
Now the King drinkes to *Hamlet*. Come, begin,
And you the Iudges beare a wary eye.

    Ham. Come on sir.
    Laer. Come on sir.   *They play.*
    Ham. One.
    Laer. No.
    Ham. Iudgement.
    Osr. A hit, a very palpable hit.
    Laer. Well: againe.
    King. Stay, giue me drinke.
Hamlet, this Pearle is thine,
Here's to thy health. Giue him the cup,
                Trumpets sound, and shot goes off.
    Ham. Ile play this bout first, set by a while.
Come: Another hit; what say you?
    Laer. A touch, a touch, I do confesse.
    King. Our Sonne shall win.
    Qu. He's fat, and scant of breath.
Heere's a Napkin, rub thy browes,
The Queene Carowses to thy fortune, *Hamlet*.
    Ham. Good Madam.
    King. Gertrude, do not drinke.
    Qu. I will my Lord;
I pray you pardon me.
    King. It is the poyson'd Cup, it is too late.

From the First Folio text of 1623, probably set up from a playhouse
manuscript. Note the minor differences.

C

King. Set me the Stopes of Wine upon that Table :
If *Hamlet* give the firſt, or ſecond hit,
Or quit in anſwer of a third exchange,
Let all the Battlements their Ordnance fire.
The King ſhall drink to *Hamlet's* better breath,
And in the Cup an Union ſhall he throw
Richer than that, which four ſucceſſive Kings
In *Denmark's* Crown have worn. Give me the Cups,
And let the Kettle to the Trumpets ſpeak,
The Trupets to the Canoneer without,
The Canons to the Heav'ns, the Heav'n to Earth,
Now the King drinks to *Hamlet.* Come, begin,
And you the Judges bear a wary Eye.

   Ham. Come on, Sir.
   Laer. Come on, Sir.   [*They play.*
   Ham. One.
   Laer. No.
   Ham. Judgment.
   Oſr. A hit, a very palpable hit.
   Laer. Well—— again——
   King. Stay, give me drink. *Hamlet,* this Pearl is thine,
Here's to thy health. Give him the Cup.
                    [*Trumpet ſound, Shot goes off.*
   Ham. I'll play this bout firſt, set it by a while.
Come——another hit——what ſay you ?   [*They Play again.*
   Laer. A touch, a touch, I do confeſs.
   King. Our Son ſhall win.
   Queen. He's fat, and ſcant of breath.
Here's a Napkin, rub thy brows,
The Queen carouſes to thy fortune, *Hamlet.*
   Ham. Good Madam——
   King. *Gertrude,* do not drink.
   Queen. I will, my Lord ; I pray you pardon me.
   King. It is the poiſon'd Cup, it is too late.   [*Aſide.*

From Nathaniel Rowe's edition of 1709. Note the regulariſed text and stage directions, and the revised punctuation.

D

King. Set me the stoups of wine upon that table.
If Hamlet give the first or second hit,
Or quit in answer of the third exchange,
Let all the battlements their ordnance fire;
The king shall drink to Hamlet's better breath;
And in the cup an union shall he throw,
Richer than that which four successive kings
In Denmark's crown have worn.   Give me the cups;
And let the kettle to the trumpet speak,
The trumpet to the cannoneer without,
The cannons to the heavens, the heavens to earth,
'Now the king drinks to Hamlet!' Come, begin;
And you, the judges, bear a wary eye.

   Ham. Come on, sir.

   Laer.   Come, my lord. [*They play.*

   Ham.   One.

   Laer.   No.

   Ham.   Judgment.

   Osr. A hit, a very palpable hit.

   Laer.   Well; again.

   King. Stay; give me drink.   Hamlet, this
      pearl is thine;
Here's to thy health.   Give him the cup.

     [*Trumpets sound; and cannon shot off within.*
   Ham. I'll play this bout first; set it by awhile.
Come—[*They play.*] Another hit; what say you ?

   Laer. A touch, a touch, I do confess.

   King. Our son shall win.

   Queen.   He's fat, and scant of breath.
Here, Hamlet, take my napkin, rub thy brows;
The queen carouses to thy fortune, Hamlet.

   Ham. Good madam !

   King.   Gertrude, do not drink.

   Queen. I will, my lord; I pray you, pardon me.

   King. [*Aside.*] It is the poison'd cup ! it is
      too late.

From the Oxford *Shakespeare,* dated 1928.   This is the form most
familiar to most modern readers.

King. Set me the stoups of wine upon that table.
If *Hamlet* give the first or second hit,
Or quit in answer of the third exchange,
Let all the battlements their ordnance fire.
The king shall drink to Hamlet's better breath,
And in the cup an union shall he throw,
Richer than that which four successive kings
In Denmark's crown have worn; give me the cups,
And let the kettle to the trumpet speak,
The trumpet to the cannoneer without,
The cannons to the heavens, the heaven to earth,
' Now the king drinks to Hamlet.' Come, begin,
And you, the judges, bear a wary eye.

> *(the cups are set at his side; trumpets sound;*
> *Hamlet and Laertes take their stations)*

Hamlet. Come on, sir.
Laertes.   Come, my lord.
>   *They play*

Hamlet.   One !
Laertes.   No.
Hamlet.   Judgement ?
Osric. A hit, a very palpable hit.

> [*they break off; the kettle-drum sounds, the trumpets*
> *blow, and a cannon-shot is heard without*

Laertes.   Well, again.
King. Stay, give me drink. [*a servant fills a cup*]
     Hamlet, [*he holds up a jewel*], this pearl is thine.
Here's to thy health !   [*he drinks and then seems to cast*
>   *the pearl into the cup*

     Give him the cup.
Hamlet. I'll play this bout first, set it by a while.

> [*the servant sets it on a table behind him*

Come.

>   *They play again*

     Another hit !   What say you ?
Laertes. A touch, a touch, I do confess't.

>   [*they break off*

King. Our son shall win.
Queen.   He's fat, and scant of breath.

Here, Hamlet, take my napkin, rub thy brows.
> [*she gives it him, and going to the table*
> *takes up his cup of wine*

The queen carouses to thy fortune, Hamlet.

Hamlet. Good madam !

King. Gertrude, do not drink.

Queen. I will, my lord, I pray you pardon me.
> [*she drinks and offers the cup to Hamlet*

King. It is the poisoned cup, it is too late !

From *The New Shakespeare*, edited by J. Dover Wilson. The latest method of editing Shakespeare.

A modern editor is therefore faced with many new problems, especially in producing an edition intended for the general reader. There is so much interest in the recent work of scholars that the older " authorised version " is no longer suitable. For the student an exact facsimile of the Quarto or Folio is the most valuable text. But the general reader is troubled by the old tall s which so closely resembles an f, and can lead to awkward mistakes. The use of u for v, i for j and other Elizabethan practices such as y^e for the or y^m for them. An editor must compromise both in printing and in arrangement.

In the "Penguin" *Shakespeares* the text follows the original very closely. The place-headings which were added to the beginnings of scenes by editors of the 18th century have been abandoned. Act and scene divisions are marked only for reference. Stage directions follow the original as closely as possible. The old punctuation has been kept unless it seems obviously impossible.

Such principles seem simple until an editor tries to carry them out. Even when there is only one original text—the Folio—there are difficult problems. In *Macbeth*, for instance, the Folio text sometimes prints short lines of verse. Editors have often joined them to make complete blank-verse lines, rearranging the rest of the speech. Shakespeare sometimes began a blank-verse speech with a half-line. This irritated editors, who shift the lines up to make them look better, until they come to some line which cannot be moved. Then they leave it as a broken line and start again.

When a Folio text is closely studied it is clear that much of *Macbeth* is not written in formal blank verse at all, but in a free, rhythmic verse ; so also is *Antony and Cleopatra*. But readers and even critics have not realised that Shakespeare often wrote in a free verse, because they are not accustomed to use the Folio.

For an instance : After the murder of Duncan, Lady Macbeth and her husband are surprised by the knocking ; she tries to bring him to his senses. In the authorised text the speech appears :

" My hands are of your colour, but I shame
  To wear a heart so white.—[*Knocking within*] I hear a knocking
  At the south entry ; retire we to our chamber ;
  A little water clears us of this deed ;
  How easy it is, then ! Your constancy
  Hath left you unattended. [*Knocking within*] Hark ! more knocking.
  Get on your night-gown, lest occasion call us,
  And show us to be watchers. Be not lost
  So poorly in your thoughts."

The quick, jerky utterance is much more effectively shown in the Folio printing :

> " My hands are of your colour : but I shame
> To wear a heart so white.
>
> *Knock*
>
> I hear a knocking at the south entry :
> Retire we to our chamber :
> A little water clears us of this deed.
> How easy is it then ?   Your constancy
> Hath left you unattended.
>
> *Knock*
>
> Hark, more knocking.
> Get on your nightgown, lest occasion call us,
> And show us to be watchers : be not lost
> So poorly in your thoughts."

The editor's worst difficulties come when there are one or more early texts : a Quarto and a Folio. In some instances the printer of the Folio used a printed Quarto and made little alteration.

One of the most difficult texts is *King Lear*. There are about five hundred differences of reading between the Quarto and Folio.   The Folio text, as a close examination shows, was set up from a copy of the Quarto most carefully corrected.   Presumably, therefore, the Folio gives what its editors regarded as the best version.   Sometimes, however, the Quarto is better than the Folio and often entirely different.   Hitherto editors have simply followed one another, choosing their readings at haphazard from either text, and not always the better reading.

There is a good example in the opening scene. When Lear turns to Cordelia to give her judgment, according to the Quarto version he says :

> " but now our joy,
> Although the last, not least in our dear love,
> What can you say to win a third, more opulent
> Than your sisters' ? "

In the Folio the version is :

> " Now our Joy,
> Although our last and least ; to whose young love,
> The Vines of France, and Milk of Burgundy,
> Strive to be interest.   What can you say, to draw
> A third, more opulent than your sisters ?   Speak."

Editors choose the Quarto reading, arguing, presumably, that Shakespeare would have chosen the common, proverbial phrase " last but not least." Thereby they miss the whole point of the speech. Cordelia was presented as a little creature, physically overshadowed by Goneril and Regan. Lear cannot understand how so small a body should seemingly contain so brazen a heart.

When such problems occur, as they do frequently, an editor can only follow his own judgment. In general he should be guided by principles, but he soon finds that he cannot follow them consistently.

He can only comfort himself with the bleak thought that he will have the same reward or punishment as all others who write or edit books. If his work pleases, it will succeed ; if not it will disappear. Editing Shakespeare is, indeed, more of an art than a science.

A SHORT READING LIST

I. GENERAL

A Companion to Shakespeare Studies. Edited by Harley Granville-
Barker and G. B. Harrison. Cambridge Press.
   An Introduction to the various branches of modern Shake-
speare study, each chapter being written by an expert.

Shakespeare's England : An Account of the Life and Manners of his Age.
Edited by Sir Walter Raleigh. 2 vols. Oxford Press.
   A series of studies, each written by an expert, of the many
activities and branches of life in Shakespeare's England.

William Shakespeare : A Study of Facts and Problems. By Sir E. K.
Chambers. 2 vols. Oxford Press.
   Though hardly suitable for general reading, this is an in-
dispensable reference book for the serious student. There is
an abridged edition called *A Short Life of Shakespeare : With the
Sources.*

The Elizabethan Journals : 1592–1603. By G. B. Harrison. 3 vols.
in one. Routledge.
   A day-by-day account of those things most talked of during
these years.

II. THE THEATRE

The Elizabethan Theatre. By Sir E. K. Chambers. 4 vols. Oxford
Press.
   An indispensable book for students.
Henslowe's Diary. 2 vols. Edited by W. W. Greg. Sidgwick &
Jackson.
Henslowe's Papers. Edited by W. W. Greg. Sidgwick & Jackson.
   The most important and interesting collection of original
documents covering the Elizabethan playhouse.

A SHORT READING LIST

III. THE SHAKESPEARE TEXT

Shakespeare's Fight with the Pirates. By A. W. Pollard. Cambridge Press.

Mainly responsible for the modern interest in textual study.

Shakespeare's Hand in " Sir Thomas More." By A. W. Pollard and others. Cambridge Press.

An examination of the reasons for believing that three pages in this manuscript play are in Shakespeare's autograph.

The New Shakespeare. Edited by Sir Arthur Quiller and J. Dover Wilson. Cambridge Press.

This text is the result of modern textual theories. New volumes appear from time to time. The first—*The Tempest*—contains a general introduction setting out the principles followed in the text.

IV. CRITICISM

Shakespeare. By Sir Walter Raleigh. "English Men of Letters" Series.

One of the best of the general studies of Shakespeare.

The Approach to Shakespeare. By J. W. Mackail. Oxford Press.

A useful general introduction to the critical study of Shakespeare.

Shakespearian Tragedy. By A. C. Bradley. Macmillan.

The most elaborate critical study of the four great tragedies.

Shakespeare's Workmanship. By Sir A. T. Quiller-Couch. Cambridge Press.

A lively demonstration that Shakespeare was a man of the theatre.

Prefaces to Shakespeare. By Harley Granville-Barker. Sidgwick & Jackson.

SERIES I. *Love's Labour's Lost. Julius Caesar. King Lear.*
SERIES II. *Romeo and Juliet. The Merchant of Venice. Antony and Cleopatra.*
SERIES III. *Hamlet.*

The most important critical examination of these plays—from the point of view of the producer and student of the stage—that has yet appeared.

INTRODUCING SHAKESPEARE

Shakespeare Criticism. (From the beginnings to Carlyle.) Edited by D. Nichol Smith. "World's Classics."

Shakespeare Criticism 1919–1935. Edited by Anne Bradby. "World's Classics."

The first gives generous extracts from the critics of the 17th, 18th and early 19th centuries; the second reprints a number of studies by modern critics.

THE PENGUIN SHAKESPEARE

Edited by G. B. HARRISON

TITLES ALREADY PUBLISHED:

" Shakespeare for sixpence is well enough, but this is Shakespeare well edited and
well produced; books as bright as new pins, planned with care. Explanatory notes
are placed at the end—very wisely, seeing that this is Shakespeare for the million. The
notes are sound and often refreshingly forthright ; with the general reader in mind,
the editor rightly refrains from considering too curiously. Altogether an admirable
enterprise and one that seems certain to further the progress of the Penguin Books."
—*Sunday Times.*

THE NEW PELICANS

March 1939

LATEST
"SPECIALS"

Others Coming.

THE NEW PENGUINS

January 1939

March 1939

PENGUIN BOOKS

COMPLETE LIST OF PUBLICATIONS TO THE END OF 1938

FICTION *orange covers*

" Bartimeus "	A Tall Ship
Arnold Bennett	
	The Grand Babylon Hotel
Algernon Blackwood	The Centaur
Phyllis Bottome	Private Worlds
Marjorie Bowen	The Glen O' Weeping
Ernest Bramah	Kai Lung's Golden Hours
Ann Bridge	Peking Picnic
Louis Bromfield	
	The Strange Case of Miss Annie Spragg
D. K. Broster	Sir Isumbras at the Ford
J. L. Campbell	The Miracle of Peille
G. K. Chesterton	
	The Man Who Was Thursday
Susan Ertz	Madame Claire
	Now East, Now West
William Faulkner	Soldiers' Pay
E. M. Forster	A Passage to India
Leonhard Frank	Carl and Anna
Crosbie Garstin	The Owls' House
Stella Gibbons	Cold Comfort Farm
John Hampson	
	Saturday Night at the Greyhound
Ian Hay	A Safety Match
Robert Hichens	(2 vols.) Paradine Case
James Hilton	Dawn of Reckoning
Constance Holme	The Lonely Plough
Claude Houghton	Chaos Is Come Again
	I Am Jonathan Scrivener
W. W. Jacobs	Deep Waters
M. R. James	Ghost Stories of an Antiquary
Sinclair Lewis	Mantrap
Rose Macaulay	Crewe Train
Denis Mackail	Greenery Street
Ethel Mannin	Children of the Earth
	Ragged Banners
R. H. Mottram	The Spanish Farm
Beverley Nichols	Self
Liam O'Flaherty	The Informer
D. Kilham Roberts (editor)	
	Penguin Parade (1)
	Penguin Parade (2)
	Penguin Parade (3)
	Penguin Parade (4)
E. Arnot Robertson	Four Frightened People
V. Sackville-West	The Edwardians

Ramon Sender	Seven Red Sundays
Graham Seton	The W Plan
Beatrice Kean Seymour	Youth Rides Out
Edward Shanks	(2 vols.) Queer Street
Ignazio Silone	Fontamara
Osbert Sitwell	Before the Bombardment
Somerville and Ross	
	Some Experiences of an Irish R.M.
Alan Steele (editor)	
	Selected Modern Short Stories (1)
	Selected Modern Short Stories (2)
Ralph Straus	The Unseemly Adventure
Tchehov	Tales from Tchehov
Angela Thirkell	Wild Strawberries
Edward Thompson	An Indian Day
Ben Travers	A Cuckoo in the Nest
Hugh Walpole	Mr. Perrin and Mr. Traill
Sylvia Townsend Warner	Lolly Willowes
Evelyn Waugh	Black Mischief
	Decline and Fall
	Vile Bodies
Edith Wharton	Ethan Frome
P. G. Wodehouse	My Man Jeeves
E. H. Young	William
Francis Brett Young	The Crescent Moon

CRIME FICTION *green covers*

Anthony Armstrong	Ten Minute Alibi
H. C. Bailey	Mr. Fortune, Please
E. C. Bentley	Trent's Last Case
Anthony Berkeley	The Piccadilly Murder
Alice Campbell	Spider Web
John Dickson Carr	It Walks by Night
	The Waxworks Murder
Agatha Christie	The Murder on the Links
	The Mysterious Affair at Styles
G. D. H. and Margaret Cole	
	Murder at Crome House
J. J. Connington	The Dangerfield Talisman
	Death at Swaythling Court
A. Conan Doyle	
	The Hound of the Baskervilles
John Ferguson	The Man in the Dark

[Contd.

RADIO NORMANDY

Stars NEW Wavelength **274** metres

GEORGE FORMBY

BILLY COTTON

REGINALD FOORT

CARROLL LEVIS

JACK JACKSON

BEBE DANIELS & BEN LYON

JACK HYLTON

CHARLIE KUNZ

DONALD PEERS

DEBROY SOMERS

CARROLL GIBBONS

		TIMES OF TRANSMISSIONS		
SUNDAYS		7.0 a.m.	to	11.45 a.m.
		1.30 p.m.	to	7.30 p.m.
		10.0 p.m.	to	1.0 a.m.
WEEKDAYS		7.0 a.m.	to	11.30 a.m.
		2.0 p.m.	to	6.0 p.m.
		12 (Midnight)	to	1.0 a.m.
		(FRIDAY & SATURDAY until 2 a.m.)		

IBC

INTERNATIONAL BROADCASTING COMPANY LTD.

37, PORTLAND PLACE, LONDON, W.1. Telephone: LANGHAM 2000 (14 lines) Telegrams: Interbroad, London.

Richard Keverne   *The Havering Plot*
The Man in the Red Hat
The Sanfield Scandal
C. Daly King   *Obelists at Sea*
Philip Macdonald   *The Rasp*
Ngaio Marsh   *Enter a Murderer*
A. A. Milne   *The Red House Mystery*
John Rhode   *The House on Tollard Ridge*
The Murders in Praed Street
Sax Rohmer *The Mystery of Dr. Fu-Manchu*
Dorothy L. Sayers
The Documents in the Case
W. Stanley Sykes *The Missing Moneylender*
Edgar Wallace   *The Four Just Men*
H. G. Wells   *The Invisible Man*

TRAVEL & ADVENTURE *cerise covers*

J. Johnston Abraham   *The Surgeon's Log*
Edmund Blunden   *Undertones of War*
F. S. Chapman *Watkins' Last Expedition*
Apsley Cherry-Garrard
(2 vols.) *The Worst Journey in the World*
Alexandra David-Neel
With Mystics and Magicians in Tibet
Anthony Fokker   *Flying Dutchman*
Alfred Aloysius Horn   *Trader Horn*
Anne Morrow Lindbergh
North to the Orient
C. A. W. Monckton
(2 vols.) *Some Experiences of a New Guinea Resident Magistrate*
J. M. Scott *The Land that God Gave Cain*
Captain von Rintelen   *The Dark Invader*
Nora Waln   *House of Exile*

BIOGRAPHY & MEMOIRS *dark blue covers*

H. C. Armstrong
Grey Wolf (Mustafa Kemal)
Lord of Arabia (Ibn Saud)
Margot Asquith (2 vols.) *Autobiography*

E. F. Benson   *As We Were*
Charlton   *" Charlton "*
Pamela Frankau   *Find Four People*
B. H. Liddell Hart   (2 vols.) *Foch*
Ethel Mannin *Confessions and Impressions*
André Maurois   *Ariel*
Disraeli
Beverley Nichols   *Twenty-Five*
Maurice O'Sullivan
Twenty Years A-Growing

MISCELLANEOUS
yellow covers

Earl Baldwin   *On England*
Francis and Vera Meynell (editors)
(2 vols.) *The Week-end Book*
Alexander Woollcott *While Rome Burns*

DRAMA *red covers*

THE PENGUIN SHAKESPEARE, edited by Dr. G. B. Harrison; these plays, each in a separate volume with special Notes and Introductions, are available so far:

Twelfth Night	*Henry the Fifth*
Hamlet	*As You Like It*
King Lear	*A Midsummer Night's Dream*
The Tempest	*The Merchant of Venice*
Richard II	*Romeo and Juliet*
Julius Caesar	*Henry IV (part 1)*
Macbeth	*Henry IV (part 2)*
Othello	*Much Ado About Nothing*
The Sonnets	*Antony and Cleopatra*

SEVEN FAMOUS ONE-ACT PLAYS, by Alfred Sutro, A. P. Herbert, Clifford Bax Stanley Houghton, W. W. Jacobs, J. A. Ferguson, and Oliphant Down.

[Contd.

ILLUSTRATED CLASSICS ★

Art Director: Robert Gibbings;
Introductions by G. B. Harrison

Jane Austen   *Pride and Prejudice*
          (illustrated by Helen Binyon)
Robert Browning
          Selected Poems (Iain Macnab)
Daniel Defoe
          (2 vols.) *Robinson Crusoe* (J. R. Biggs)
Richard Jefferies   *The Story of My Heart*
          (Gertrude Hermes)
Herman Melville *Typee* (Robert Gibbings)
Edgar Allan Poe
     Some Tales of Mystery and Imagination
          (Douglas Percy Bliss)
Laurence Sterne
     A Sentimental Journey (Gwen Raverat)
Jonathan Swift
     Gulliver's Travels (Theodore Naish)
David Thoreau *Walden* (Ethelbert White)

PENGUIN SPECIALS

Norman Angell   *The Great Illusion—Now*
The Duchess of Atholl *Searchlight on Spain*
Phyllis Bottome   *The Mortal Storm*
Charlton, Garratt and Fletcher
          The Air Defence of Britain
G. T. Garratt   *Mussolini's Roman Empire*
S. Grant Duff   *Europe and the Czechs*
Louis Golding   *The Jewish Problem*
Lord Londonderry *Ourselves and Germany*
W. M. Macmilian
          Warning from the West Indies
Edgar Mowrer *Germany Puts the Clock Back*
          Mowrer in China
Wickham Steed   *The Press*
Geneviève Tabouis   *Blackmail or War*

PELICAN SPECIALS

Arnold Bennett   *Literary Taste*
Anthony Bertram   ★ *Design*
Arnold Haskell   ★ *Ballet*
Robert Gibbings ★ *Blue Angels and Whales*

PELICAN BOOKS

light blue covers

F. L. Allen   ★ (2 vols.) *Only Yesterday*
Clive Bell   *Civilisation*
G. D. H. Cole   *Practical Economics*
          Socialism in Evolution
J. G. Crowther
     ★ (2 vols.) *An Outline of the Universe*
Dobrée and Manwaring
               The Floating Republic
J. H. Fabre ★ *Social Life in the Insect World*
Sigmund Freud   *Totem and Taboo*
     Psychopathology of Everyday Life
Roger Fry   *Vision and Design*
J. B. S. Haldane *The Inequality of Man*
Élie Halévy   (3 vols.)
     A History of the English People in 1815
G. B. Harrison
               A Book of English Poetry
Julian Huxley   *Essays in Popular Science*
Sir James Jeans ★ *The Mysterious Universe*
R. S. Lambert (editor)   ★ *Art in England*
H. J. Laski   *Liberty in the Modern State*
H. J. and Hugh Massingham (editors)
          (2 vols.) *The Great Victorians*
W. J. Perry   *The Growth of Civilisation*
Eileen Power   ★ *Medieval People*
D. K. Roberts (editor)
          (2 vols.) *The Century's Poetry*
Bernard Shaw
     (2 vols.) *The Intelligent Woman's Guide*
Olaf Stapledon   *Last and First Men*
J. W. N. Sullivan   *Limitations of Science*
R. H. Tawney
     Religion and the Rise of Capitalism
Beatrice Webb
          (2 vols.) *My Apprenticeship*
H. G. Wells *A Short History of the World*
A. N. Whitehead
          Science and the Modern World
Leonard Woolf   *After the Deluge*
Virginia Woolf   *The Common Reader*
Sir Leonard Woolley ★ *Ur of the Chaldees*
          ★ *Digging up the Past*

★ *ILLUSTRATED*

Enquiries about advertising space in Penguin Books
should be addressed to :

E. W. PLAYER LTD., 61, Chandos Place, W.C.2.
Telephone : Temple Bar 6008-9